Top 10 Greatest Lies About Beauty

"You can 'deep-clean' your skin."

"An expensive skin care product is better
for your skin than an inexpensive product."

"A little sun won't hurt you."

"This perm will make your hair look more natural."

"This product is suitable for your age."

"Only teenagers get acne."

"This cream gets rid of wrinkles."

"The more fragrance you use,
the better you smell."

"I'll just trim your hair a little."

"This will make you look younger."

Beauty, More Than Skin Deep

by Ronda Gates

with Ethel Harms
Illustrations by Joanne Deitz Thompson

Lifestyles 4 Heart Press
Lake Oswego, Oregon

Publisher's Note
   The ideas, procedures and suggestions contained in this book are not intended to be a substitute for consulting with your physician. All matters regarding your health require medical supervision.

Publisher's Cataloging-in-Publication
(Provided by Quality Books, Inc.)

Gates, Ronda.
     Beauty : more than skin deep / by Ronda Gates with Ethel
Harms ; illustrations by Joanne Dietz. -- 1st ed.

     p. cm.
     LCCN 00-011185
     ISBN 1-878319-04-3

     1. Skin--care and hygiene. 2. Beauty, Personal. 3. Self-esteem
in women. I. Harms, Ethel. II Dietz, Joanne. III. Title.

RA778.G38 2001   646.7'042
                                                  QBI00-902043

Published by
LIFESTYLES 4 Heart Press
Lake Oswego, Oregon

*This book is dedicated to
the first beautiful woman I met,
my mother, Ruth Feldman.*

Contents

Section V: Under Your Skin

Section VI: Beyond Skin—The Invisible Factors

Preface

"Why should I write a book about beauty? Lifestyles is a health promotion education business, I'm no makeup expert."

That was the response I gave my good friend, Dianne Dunkelman, when she asked me if I could follow my effort writing *Smart Women, Strong Bones* for the Speaking of Women's Health Foundation with a book "about beauty."

"Think about it," she challenged. "You are a woman, a fitness leader who has learned that your students want to "look good," a pharmacist who understands the biochemistry of the body and the chemicals in beauty products, a student of nutrition and psychology and you love educating others about the lessons you have learned yourself. Additionally, because you lecture and are in front of cameras and the media all the time, I know you have learned the tricks of the trade to make short work of putting on makeup and dressing smart. Last but not least, you have led your life in a way that defies the concept of how a sixty-plus woman should look and act. Those are enough qualifications for me."

I still wasn't sure, but agreed to let her know in a week or so. I began my decision-making process by contemplating reasons I would want to tackle writing a book I hadn't planned to write.

I began writing when I was very young. I have fond memories of Fifth grade when Mother Dorothea insisted each sentence I wrote must be diagrammed. Those puzzles, spelling bees, and the power of words intrigued me. My interest in science propelled me career-wise, but my most useful life-learning high school classes were shorthand (to take notes quickly about anything), typing (to quickly put my thoughts on paper), and a class based on the book *Word Power Made Easy* (to bring creativity to what I wrote for myself and others).

As an adult my first non-academic writing attempt brought order to the policies and procedures of the pharmacies that employed me. When I switched careers and started a fitness business, I wrote manuals for contractors and clients, and took graduate classes where essay requirements loosened my creativity.

In the mid-eighties, I began a professional relationship with a successful writer of fitness books. Because, in college, he was told his writing would never amount to anything, he took great pride in his ability to create several best sellers.

I was eager to capture this skill myself. In this mentoring environment I was encouraged to bring some writing to the office for review. I was nervous, but excited, when I arrived with several health related articles and a tape recorder to make sure I didn't miss a word of his reaction. He leaned back in his office chair, put his feet on the desk, and began reading. Soon he was groaning. "This is terrible." "You should write for the public health service." And the worst: "It's boring."

He tossed the pages on his desk and said, "Write like you talk."

That was it! It sounded simple, but it wasn't.

Fifteen years later I'm living proof that we can improve skills important to us. That mentor and I co-authored a best-selling book in 1996. It is one of five that have my name on the cover.

Most of us believe it is possible to write only about something we know intimately or for which we hold credentials that define us as an expert. It's not necessarily so. Thanks to the internet, books, courses at community colleges, conferences, and life, anyone can become an expert on anything. Making it fun to read is the challenge. I start with a passion to ferret fact from fiction about a subject that interests me then think, "what would my girlfriends want to know."

When it comes to knowledge about the aging process my quest began years ago. It started in 1978, when I traded my white pharmacy coat for a pair of athletic shoes and danced into a "new" career in the health promotion field. I discovered that women signed up for my corporate fitness classes because they wanted to lose weight and look better. Soon they experienced a paradigm shift. The benefits to their regular exercise program included an unexpected elevation in self-esteem precipitated by feeling not only physically, but also mentally, socially, emotionally and spiritually better about themselves and their lives.

Regardless, with "maturity," that self-esteem soon engaged in a war with changing physical bodies that showed the effects of gravity, sun and the hard knocks of life. Professionally I had the good fortune to cross paths with forward thinkers who talked about a forthcoming "agequake" and the development of products to ease baby boomers into their "retirement" years. It precipitated a deeper search for knowledge about the emerging beauty care market—especially in relation to the chemistry, biochemistry and physiology angle that was the foundation of my professional life. I was not disappointed. A trickle of longstanding products, like my favorite Oil of Olay, were soon joined by a flood of remedies for "aging" skin and a body that no longer recovered quickly from any challenge. That quest for knowledge continues.

That is why, ultimately, I realized the answer to Dianne's request to write about beauty from the inside out and the outside in was, "I can do that."

I had a major weakness for the project. I was not competent to give advice to women who wanted to enhance their features. I called Ethel Harms, a model, stylist, dear friend, and a stunningly beautiful woman, from her glowing skin right down to the center of her lovely heart. Ethel and I, twenty five years earlier, forged a friendship when our paths crossed at ridiculously early and late hours as we supported our sons' love of ice hockey. I'd drag myself into the rink half dressed and barely awake, and find Ethel, despite the ungodly hour and the bone-chilling damp cold, always looking like the preverbal million bucks. This woman knew, and knows, how to put a good face forward. When we needed an illustrator Ethel said, "I know a talented young (to us) woman." The rest is history.

This book was truly a collaboration. Our working premise was a deeply shared belief that all the makeup, cosmetic surgery, and dressing for your role in life comes off as, frankly, phony, if your entire organism isn't also radiating physical, emotional and spiritual health.

In addition to illustrations, the book includes useful charts and savvy tips to emphasize important points. If you like personal stories you can thumb through the book, look for Her Story, highlighted in italics, and read stories, applicable to the content of that chapter, about women just like you and me.

Do you want to know?:

"What creams work to soften skin toughened by the sun?"

"Why doesn't red lipstick brighten my face anymore?"

"If an antioxidant food works miracles on the inner body will an antioxidant based cream work miracles on my outer body?"

"Why, when I look at my Thanksgiving turkey, do I think about my neck instead of a full stomach?"

"How much of beauty is and isn't skin deep?"

Then fasten your seat belts. We are about to shower you with information that will work wonders with your wrappers and help you look and feel better about one of life's certainties—aging. I'll warn you in advance, beauty is more than skin deep.

Ronda

Acknowledgements

Every book is a collaboration. In addition to Ethel Harms who spent many hours sharpening years of experience into the words that describe makeup techniques and Joanne Deitz Thompson whose extraordinary talent made a book about beauty beautiful, others contributed in big and small ways:

Tami Jewell, the project management queen, who also coordinated my life during the writing process and who, when I needed it most, thrust Haley and Lilly through my door.

John Kalbrener, who assures my writing stays upbeat.

Covert Bailey, who first told me, "write like you talk."

Beverly Whipple, my co-author for *Smart Women, Strong Bones,* whose eagle eye finds errors everyone else may miss.

Diane Kemp, Heather Cullen, Kristin Kemp and Peggy Depuy for offering feedback on content.

Dave Fabik for always being ready to remedy a computer glitch.

Sheryl Mehary, my desktop publishing whiz, who not only is gifted in her craft, but a patient guide to those of us who love to put words on paper.

Additionally, I owe thanks to the Speaking of Women's Health staff who, day after day, do more than their job by providing support and feedback to me as I write and speak for their organization nationwide.

And, most of all, to Dianne Dunkelman, founder and president of Speaking of Women's Health, whose encouragement, enthusiasm, confidence and support continues to inspire me to write about women's health issues. Our professional relationship evolved quickly into friendship. I could not be more grateful for her cheerful feedback, for laughing with me through the review process and exemplifying, always, the meaning of girl friend.

Introduction: Her Story

In The Beginning

Several years ago, a popular magazine published a series of pictures that used computer technology to show how a woman's face and body would age as she moved into the next decade of her life. With computer "morphing" each progressive image revealed how an obviously vibrant and active woman acquired pockets of loose and sagging skin - despite an obviously well exercised and well-toned body. As I turned each page, instead of getting depressed, I was delighted to discover that though the image showed post-menopausal breasts smaller than those of me and my hormone-subsidized peers, my body was typical for women my age.

I pulled out those soon dog-eared pictures at all kinds of gatherings for women. Then, on a whim, I gathered a group of eight girlfriends aged 36 to 72 for a weekend beauty retreat at a home in the mountains of Oregon. I asked them to bring as many photos as possible of themselves at different times in their life plus pictures of five women they perceived to be great looking. The weekend called for long vigorous walks, healthy eating, manicures, facials, the services of a masseuse and the safety of friendship where innermost secrets and fantasies could be shared.

On Saturday, after brunch, I pulled out my computer-morphed pictures and after we oooed and aahed over them we spread our personal photos over the table. They precipitated memories—and questions—all weekend long.

Each of us had photos documenting our earliest years as healthy looking infants snuggled in the arms of a parent. Soon we were sitting in a stroller, then learning to stand, walk and play— in the sunshine! Others cared for our skin—Ivory soap and baby powder or lotion was the regimen at my home. Organs under- neath that soft skin were nourished with food choices that reflected our parent's nutrition values. *My friends' experiences reflected the background of their family values, their decade of birth and their ethnicity but were similar.*

We laughed about early "skin memories." Most included bubble baths shared with a sibling. I remembered a vigorous scrubbing, with pumice soap, after I lovingly brought home a bouquet of poison ivy flowers I picked for my mother.

It wasn't long before we realized that skin was both intimately private and blatantly public. In our teens it seemed that every cut, scrape, bruise, scar, pimple and bump was visible. Despite our diverse ages now, our teen years included struggles with large pores, blackheads and acne. That precipitated the picking and poking period and intense scrutinizing of our faces in the bathroom mirror. Everyone laughed at the memories we shared about our blemish experiences. "Remember the horror of facing school with a pimple in the middle of your forehead?" Only the 36-year-old had the advantage of prescription drugs to prevent the acne scars the rest of us had etched on our face in varying degrees. Based on age we discovered we'd had different options for braces, skin protection and makeup.

Scrutiny of the face soon moved to scrutiny of the body and discovery that the internal and external manifestations of life on exposed skin could be camouflaged with clothes and makeup. If you grew up in the forties and fifties there were no long aisles or big displays of cosmetics at drug and department stores. Our choices included red lipstick and clumpy mascara. Remember the movie Grease? *Like the "pink ladies" too much makeup (or pierced ears or, God forbid, a tattoo) and you risked being labeled a slut.*

That dichotomy about makeup was a struggle each of us faced when hormones triggered our first experiences with our sexuality. Much seemed to be riding on a first impression about how attractive we were perceived to be, not to mention that it was through the skin that we became aware of the pleasures of a caress or kiss.

In college, we raced to dormitory courtyards where, with friends and fashion magazines, we beached ourselves in itsy bitsy teeny-weenie bikinis in an effort to tan every possible inch of our skin. To accelerate the process we slathered ourselves with baby oils and cocoa butter or, if our allowance permitted, the new suntan enhancement creams. There was no talk of SPF or dermatologists preaching about sun damaged skin back then. So, we rigged tin foil reflectors to redirect and magnify the sun's rays-a strategy that often produced sunburn. My eldest friend admitted that her love of the sun might be what contributed to a dangerous skin cancer, melanoma, on her back thirty years earlier. We admitted we'd envied our dark-skinned friends who made "black is beautiful" easy to understand until we learned, that weekend, from a black sister, that, with the exception of tanning, our skin struggles were the same. We also learned that her dark skin made blemishes, scars, and other skin injuries more visible.

My college experience had an interesting skin twist to it because I was a Pharmacy major. In those days (1957-61) that included compounding cosmetic products to cover, heal and enhance beauty. I became a resource for the girls who wanted special lotions and potions we hoped would cover and cure acne, heal fever blisters and make skin glow. To temper blemishes we avoided chocolate and greasy foods and, later in life, mourned when we learned these favorites hadn't contributed to our acne after all.

We learned that although we were each unique individuals, we shared many experiences in common. The oldest in the group married at the youngest age and our 36-year-old was still unmarried. Those of us with children agreed that pregnancy was when we learned about varicose veins, stretch marks and sleep deprivation.

I lived in Denver where the thinner air made dry skin and chapped lips a daily problem. In the pharmacy I was dispensing products prescribed for patients whose emotional problems were manifested in a variety of skin rashes. When queried, my doctor friends expressed wonder at the frequency with which medical conditions, including those of the skin, appeared and disappeared as their patient's psychological states changed.

By the 1990's things were completely different and the cosmetic business was a multi-billion-dollar international industry. My youngest friends were reaping the benefits. They'd used SPF based makeup for years, but my forty-something friends were seeking camouflage strategies for prominent under eye circles and "crow's feet" and asking the visiting esthetician, "Is this an age spot?"

Baby boomers were at an age when the cumulative experiences of their physical and emotional life were playing themselves out on their skin—especially the skin on their face. Like the woman in my computer-generated picture, aging skin sagged. It also became thicker, drier and rough on the surface but thinner overall. It no longer healed quickly. Frequently used facial expressions became permanent etchings thanks to multiple daily contractions of surrounding muscles. All of us had lied about our age at least once and we joked as we recalled mothers who erased birth dates on their driver's licenses or still claimed to be thirty-nine.

Everyone in our group had visited a cosmetic surgeon for a variety of reasons including wart removal, eyelid surgery (blepharoplasty), liposuction, a peel or a S.M.A.S., (commonly known as a facelift). Everyone over age fifty had been treated for a pre-cancerous lesion or basal skin cancer.

In fact, fear of skin cancers added more worry lines. We'd discovered that the sun is skin's worst enemy. It not only causes cancer, it degrades skin texture, tone and strength. Allergic reactions, bacteria, chemical and environmental irritants, emotional issues, hormones, sleep patterns, viruses and, most of all, heredity, cumulatively affected the condition of our face and body skin suit.

As we enter the twenty-first century, a woman's life expectancy is close to eighty. Each morning we watch the irrepressible NBC weatherman, Willard Scott, feature elder citizens still living active lives.

Their faces and the discovery that good health habits early in life are significant factors in their longevity awe us. When we think about it, clearly a fundamental foundation of their outward appearance is — and we've all heard it before — their attitude.

That was, we agreed after sharing the pictures of ladies we admired, the most important lesson we learned about beauty. Early in life it was about skin and clothes and hair and makeup. However, we felt that real life began at forty. That's when we truly awoke to the challenge of our life. The scripts of our first adulthood were discarded with self-discovery and, following that, self-empowerment.

Sure, we sat in the sun. In fact, we did a lot of things that "if we knew then what we know now" might have precipitated different choices. We married, divorced, remarried or stayed single. We nursed sick children and sick parents. Some of us learned lessons of life early and some of us learned later. All of us continue to learn. Regardless of the traffic jams of life, in the end we agreed we are beautiful because we choose to be visionaries instead of victims, we rely on resiliency over submission and we opt for optimism over pessimism.

We have survived hardships, celebrated victories, converted foes to friends, were mentored and then became mentors. We learned how to capitalize on lonely times, were willing to ask for help when we needed it and learned when to accept and when to discard advice. We realized that giving help to others helps ourselves. Eight women with backgrounds of different faiths also agreed that spirituality, something we can't physically put our hands on or see with our eyes, does exist. Tapping into that is what makes us feel beautiful even when we have a bad hair day, feel bloated or can't get our face on right. Regardless of our age, we want to be the best we can be whether we are in the youth of our first, second or third adulthood. We refuse to adopt the caricature of a matron who wears conservative clothes and shoes, subdued colors and understated makeup.

Today, aging includes looking good and feeling good. Understanding how skin works, what happens when it doesn't, and how to care for it, is the first step on the journey toward understanding, then practicing, how we can be our own most beautiful self, inside and out. Add a dash of makeup, a touch of style, some health maximizing exercise, more vitamin rich than nutrient poor food and, most importantly, good friends. Top it off with the cream of life — loving the age you are becoming by embracing a positive attitude, positive regard and skills for enhancing self-esteem.

Indeed, from the day we're born until the day we die, beauty is more than skin deep.

Section I

Meeting Your Skin

"*I know from my reading that I have approximately 263 bones and 600 muscles in my body. A scientist can inform me that I am a microcosm of the universe, containing 92 elements of the cosmos in my body. But play tells me that I am a living miracle, that I am not ordinary, that I am by creation more marvelous than all the statistics ever compiled and categorized.*"

Tim Hansel

1

Skin Structure

When you were in grammar school you probably learned the names of the major organs of the body. If asked today, "What are the most important organs of the body?" you would probably list those you've heard contribute most significantly to your health: "heart," "lungs," "colon," "liver," "kidneys" or "brain." There are, of course, other important organs that could be added to your list. But most people would probably neglect adding the biggest, most visible and one of the more important organs of the body: "skin."

Skin Is Big Stuff

If your skin could be laid out on a table it would cover about 18.2 square feet and weigh approximately six pounds. This strong waterproof sack is your body's first line of defense. It protects bones and other organs, perspires to help eliminate waste and cool us when we are hot and produces an oily secretion that plays a significant role in providing a barrier against anything that attempts to invade it. It has a rich supply of sensitive nerve endings that respond to touch and temperature to help you navigate through your environment. As a result, blood vessels *dilate* to provide heat and fluids to heal injuries or *contract* to maintain vital life functions.

The Five Senses

Seeing   Hearing
Smelling   Tasting
           TOUCH

Skin varies in thickness. It is thinnest on the eyelids and thickest on the palms of our hands and the soles of our feet. Continuous pressure over any part of the skin causes it to thicken, creating a callus that provides it with additional protection.

Healthy skin is slightly moist, soft, flexible and free of disease. Its texture is smooth and its color, which varies depending on the amount of pigment it contains, looks healthy. It is elastic, resilient and under normal conditions renews itself every 28 to 30 days when we are young. By the time we are well into our sixties skin turnover has declined and can take up to fifty days to renew itself.

When there is something physically or emotionally wrong with us, it often shows in our skin. On the other hand, an unsightly skin disease can precipitate emotional problems that can cause self-esteem to plummet.

Most important of all may be the role skin plays as a mirror to you and the outside world. When you are well nourished, in good physical shape, emotionally stable, well rested and keeping your skin clean and moisturized, it glows. This is skin that needs little makeup in natural light but can be enhanced with carefully applied cosmetics and skin care products. If you choose, instead, to be poorly nourished, out of shape, emotionally stressed, chronically tired or sun drenched, no amount of makeup can cover the damage.

Overriding all of this is attitude. Spend time with someone with a sunny disposition and they become beautiful despite any visible flaws. Likewise, a bad attitude can transcend the features of the most beautiful woman making her the loneliest person in the world. In other words, *beauty is more than skin deep.*

Acknowledging that, let's delve deeper into what makes up the skin you are in, how it renews itself, how it is characterized and colored and discuss the controllable and uncontrollable factors that cause it to change as it ages.

Skin Savvy

Skin is thinnest on the eyelids and thickest on the palms of the hands and the soles of the feet.

2

Skin Study 101

In the Beginning

Everyone's skin starts out baby soft and smooth. Soon this living, breathing, constantly changing organ is subjected to the bumps, bruises and other injuries of youth. If disease-free, skin is visibly altered for the first time at puberty. Hormonal fluctuations begin with the first menstrual cycle and continue through pregnancy then menopause when our estrogen levels take a serious dip and our skin becomes thinner, drier and less supple. In the meantime, other factors

The Dorling Kindersley publishing company sells beautiful books called Eyewitness Visual Dictionaries. All are awesome but *The Visual Dictionary of the Human Body*, filled with realistic photo-like drawings of every part of our body, may be the most awesome of all.

Their illustration of the skin reveals it is, in fact, a complex structure that gives true meaning to the miracle of life.

from our internal and external environment also alter its texture and condition. If we want to understand why women who age chronologically at the same rate have skin that ages visibly at an individual pace, and what creates the strident changes in our skin, it is best to start by examining the structure of skin and the role played by each of its layers.

There are two layers to skin: the bottom layer is called the dermis and the upper layer is the epidermis (*epi* = outer; *dermis* = skin).

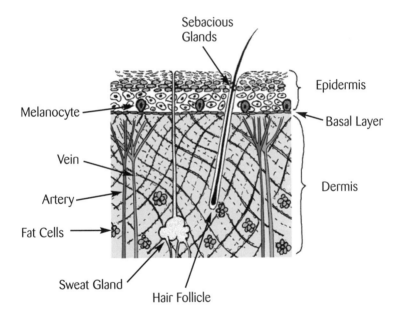

The Epidermis: Everybody Is Moulting

The layer of skin you can touch is your epidermis. Although it is thinner than a sheet of tissue paper it is, itself, multi-layered. The bottom layer of the epidermis is where new cells are born when basal (bottom) cells divide. These new cells age and get pushed upward by still newer cells because basal cells work 24 hrs. a day, seven days a week. When they reach the top of the skin these cells are flat, dried-out and composed primarily of a lifeless protein called keratin. These "dead" skin cells sit on top of the skin until they flake off or are removed when:

✓ you take a bath that washes them away
✓ you scrub or exfoliate your skin
✓ you towel off after a bath, shower or swim
✓ clothing rubs against your skin
✓ they simply fall off on their own

Both the skin waiting to be sloughed off and the new skin provide protection to underlying layers.

Everyone is born with the same number of melanocyte cells that determine the pigment, or color, of your skin. The difference lies in the amount and concentration of the melanin they produce. It is your genes that determine the amount and concentration of the melanin in *your* skin. That combination is responsible for establishing whether your skin will be pale and white or dark and almost black or the full range of combinations in between.

In between the epidermis and the layer underneath, the dermis, is a barrier layer called the basal membrane. This is the layer that prevents most commercial anti-wrinkle remedies from penetrating to a level where they might have significant effects.

Skin Savvy

An esthetician who provides professional skin care is allowed to work ONLY on the epidermal layer of the skin.

The Dermis: Everyone Is Changing

Ninety percent of your skin lies under the epidermis. This thicker layer, called the dermis, is often described as your "true" skin because it is a flourishing beehive of activity where most of the skin's "work" is done. The primary structure of the dermis is a dense meshwork of two kinds of protein-based fibers—collagen and elastin—which are cleverly woven together to form a supporting mesh. Collagen and elastin fibers are the source of skin strength and elasticity. They also contribute to its suppleness and tautness. When these fibers are young and healthy, skin is resilient and regains its former shape almost immediately after it is stretched by surgery, pregnancy or changes in weight. Just like a hammock that, with use and misuse, becomes limp, the collagen and elastin fibers get damaged—especially if we spend a lot of time in the sun.

There are other important structures in the dermis of the skin including:

✓ nerves with sensitive endings that respond to touch and temperature
✓ sweat glands that regulate the temperature of the body and help eliminate waste when we perspire
✓ sebaceous glands that produce the sebum (oil) that keeps skin moist and smooth, lubricate the skin and preserve the softness of hair on the skin
✓ hair follicles
✓ tiny muscles that give us goose bumps and make our hair "stand on end"
✓ lymph and blood vessels that transport blood, nutrients, oxygen and hormones to and from the skin

The dermis of the skin cannot be nourished from the outside.

One Square Inch of Skin Contains:

1300 nerve endings that record pain
78 sensory apparatuses for heat
19,500 sensory cells at the end of nerve fibers
13 sensory apparatuses for cold
160-165 pressure apparatuses for the perception of
  touch
65 hairs
95-100 oil (sebaceous) glands
150,000 bacteria
78 yards of nerves
19 yards of blood vessels
650 sweat glands
9,500,000 cells!!

Adipose Layer: Friendly Fat

There is a another layer, underneath the dermis that is also important. Fat, or adipose tissue, protects and cushions the underlying structures, provides insulation, makes skin smooth and is the storage reservoir for the body's supply of energy. The amount of fat under your skin varies in thickness depending on your age, gender, health, diet and physical activity. Since hormones are made from and stored in fat, the amount lying under the layers of your skin can contribute significantly to what your skin looks like from the outside. There is usually no fat under thin-skinned sites like the eyelids, but lots under thick skin sites like the palms of your hands.

Under Your Skin

Your skin is a suit of sorts. This flexible sack encloses everything that makes us beautiful. If you could see one of the many charts required to illustrate the ongoing reactions that maintain the miracle of life you would respect, and treat with more dignity, this impossible to duplicate organism we call the human body. Students of anatomy and physiology spend years attempting to understand how and why it does and doesn't work. Only surgeons and their staff really see it in action. Suffice it to say that for the purpose of skin study, our inner body plays a significant, if not well understood, role.

Deep Inside

There is an invisible, deep-down, inside, part of us that is seen by no one. We talk about our eyes being the window to our soul, but we never physically *see* inside. This most important part of us is something that we feel and know intuitively. It sings to us and provides the direction to our goals. It is, in the end, what guides us. Sometimes that deep voice gets damaged or stilled, but it is always there waiting to be awakened, mobilized, challenged, molded and refined again and again. It is who we really are. It is the "more" in the phrase, "beauty is more than skin deep."

Skin Savvy
Your skin is more than a covering; it is a barometer that registers the state of your health and reveals the story of your life.

3

How New Skin Is Made

Skin Tech 101 — Short and Sweet

All cells reproduce by dividing so there are always new skin cells in the basal layer of the epidermis. These round, smooth, fluid-filled basal cells get pushed to the surface as new cells are produced underneath. As they move upward, they change dramatically. They become flatter and harder and are now called squamous cells. Cellular protein becomes more concentrated so that by the time the cells reach the surface of the skin (a process called keratinization) they are strong and waterproof and more like the hard cells of your nails than the new cells underneath them. (When you peel after sunburn, these keratinized cells are what you see.)

There are no blood vessels or nerve endings in these now outer skin cells. They do, however, have tiny openings where skin hairs, oil and sweat, which also protect the skin, can be released. The skin cells, now multi-layered like shingles on a roof, move to the very top of the skin where they are washed away with water or brushed away with towels, clothing and complexion brushes.

If your body wasn't continually regenerating skin cells you'd be skinless in about a month because it takes that long for newly formed cells to reach the surface and slough off.

However, as you age, skin regeneration slows down. It takes much longer for skin to get to the surface. As a result, the dermis gets thinner, the blood vessels in your skin get thinner and more fragile, you produce less oil and your youthful color and glow gets dimmer. Additionally, because there is damage to the skin, there are changes in how the skin "repairs" itself. The complicated process of skin repair requires years of study. That is why, when skin is visibly damaged, the best thing you can do for yourself is visit a dermatologist who can advise you whether the damage you see requires short or long term professional care, or can be managed by the savvy use of high quality, commercially available skin care products.

The good news is that with good skin care, and the wise use of new products, you can keep skin vitalized, replenish some of the moisture and strike a deal with mother nature that keeps your skin more vibrant than someone who ignores this important element of self-care.

4

Skin Type and Color

Everyone Is Different

Before a problem can be solved it must, first, be analyzed. The same is true when we are attempting to properly care for our skin. Skin analysis includes determining whether it is dry, oily or normal.

Dry skin looks and feels "taut" because it lacks moisture. People with dry skin are more likely to have obvious lines around the eyes and mouth, or on the forehead and the skin may appear dull and flaky. The advantage of dry skin is that it doesn't lend itself to skin breakouts and blemishes and can be easily hydrated with moisturizers.

Oily skin is usually shiny, especially in the T-Zone—the area across the forehead and down the nose. Pores on the face tend to be large, particularly on the cheeks. There is often an accumulation of dried skin oils around the nose and chin that contribute to a flaky texture. The disadvantage of oily skin is that it is more prone to blackheads, whiteheads or acne breakout. Draw a tissue across oily areas and it will leave a residue on the tissue. Oily skin is usually acne prone. Its advantage is its resistance to damage from rays of the sun.

Normal skin shows no overly shiny spots, feels comfortable and shows no residue when you run a tissue across it. It is neither primarily dry nor oily. Its texture is basically smooth with the pores easily visible. If you have this skin type and experience breakouts, they are probably infrequent and related to your menstrual cycle.

Most people who say they have normal skin actually have combination skin which may be slightly dry skin with a somewhat oilier area in the T-Zone. This is the most common skin type.

Sensitive skin reacts to adverse conditions in a number of ways. Typically you will see an itchy rash or dry, flaky patches on the skin surface. Most people are sensitive to something but people with very sensitive skin seem to react to everything.

Skin Savvy
An oily skinned woman shouldn't use harsh cleansers to get rid of excess oil. Instead, wash the face with mild soap more often.

What Color Am I?

As you learned earlier, everyone is born with the same number of melanocyte cells that determine the pigment, or color, of your skin. The difference lies in the amount and concentration of the melanin it produces. This genetic factor is responsible for whether your skin will be pale and white or dark and almost black or the full range of combinations in between.

Persons of Color

Ethnicity	*Skin Savvy*
Northern European (White Skin)	SPF essential to prevent skin cancers
Afro-Caribbean Skin	Skin texture and color varies considerably from one person to another; supporting bones are strong; epidermis is thicker; dermis is thicker and has more elasticity and more efficient vasodilatory system which handles heat better; dermis produces more oil; sun induced changes in skin delayed up to twenty years; rarely exhibits "crow's feet; blemishes and scars are more visible; SPF is essential to prevent skin cancers
Asian Skin	Skin texture and color varies considerably from one person to another; high percentage of melanin; keloid scarring is more apparent; skin is slightly thicker and ages more slowly; SPF is essential to prevent skin cancers
Latino Skin Southern European	Skin texture and color varies considerably from one person to another but skin with an olive tint tends to be oilier; abrasions can create an imbalance in skin color; SPF is essential to prevent skin cancers

Knowing this makes it even more perplexing, astonishing and confusing to me that anyone would judge someone based on skin color. The physical features that reflect our ethnic backgrounds are differences that deliver the gifts we receive in every aspect of life. They bring challenges and lessons we, as women, can embrace because we are beautiful.

Happily, today, all women have a wide range of choices for defining the beautiful physical gifts our genes deliver.

5

Aging Skin

Young   **Plateau**   **Prime**

It may be hard to believe, but the projected lifespan of a woman born in 1900 was only fifty years of age. Women simply died before their skin had an opportunity to wrinkle or show any of the other changes we attribute to "aging."

Things have changed. The advent of sulfa drugs and antibiotics meant those of us born in the middle of the twentieth century could expect to live into our mid-sixties. Our culture adopted the mantra, "Life begins at forty."

As this is written more than seventy-six million baby boomers have turned fifty and, with good health habits, some of us may live another fifty years. Life is beginning again and again. Guess what, girl friends, this agequake is redefining the meaning of beauty and aging.

Despite the good news, we are forced to deal with a reality. The body, in the first and second generation of extended lifespans, begins to fail us as we reach middle-age despite our best efforts to live a healthy and active life.

Like a clock winding down, cells divide more slowly as we age and those in all layers of the skin are no exception. That means slower skin turnover, thinner skin and decreased oil and sweat production, which results in scaly, drier skin. The collagen and elastin fibers that provide the supporting structure for the skin weaken and unravel so skin elasticity is seriously diminished. As the skin repair process slows, wounds heal more slowly. Furrows and wrinkles become permanent as the contracting muscles that bring character lines and expression to our face get stronger. All this is compounded by gravity, which results in drooping eyelids and jowls. Although the sun causes most skin damage attributed to aging, even people who avoid lengthy exposure to sunlight will have changes in their skin.

Nevertheless, despite that melanoma thirty years ago, my active 72-year-old girlfriend has more in common with a woman half her age than she does with someone her age who has not been active. Best of all, genes notwithstanding, she is more likely to live longer than a healthy man her age.

Agreed, we may have to suffer the consequences of exposure to the controllable and uncontrollable factors we explored in the last chapter, but as proactive creators of our own destiny we have the *choice* to do something about it.

Since we can't treat something until we name it, the chart on the next page lists signs of aging most often seen on and around our face:

As We Age:

Skin gets drier: The sebaceous (oil) glands decrease production

Skin gets thinner: subcutaneous fat shifts leaving surface skin thin

Skin sags: there is a reduction in cells that replenish collagen and elastin

Skin doesn't respond: cells that react to irritants are less responsive

Skin is less able to regulate temperature: sweat glands don't work as well so your body doesn't adjust as quickly to changes in temperature

Skin doesn't respond to sun: cells that produce melanin don't work as well so your ability to fight sun damage is decreased, producing uneven skin color

"Signs" of Aging:

Age spots
Circles under eyes
Puffy eyes
Drooping eyelids
Lines and wrinkles
Sagging skin
Skin cancers
Skin tags
Wrinkles
Uneven skin
   texture
Uneven skin tone
Dull appearance

Age Spots
(sometimes called sun spots or liver spots)

Little girls with pale skin and freckles on their hands and faces are cute. When you are older, after years of sun exposure, the flat gray, brown or black spots that appear on your face and the back of your hands are not so cute. These "age" or "liver" spots, which result from sun-induced over-production of melanin, can range from freckle size to a few inches across.

Although they may look like a cancerous growth they are harmless. Surgery is the only way to get rid of them. Although "skin-bleaching" products, which don't bleach but enhance the translucency and luminosity of skin, will lighten age spots, they take a long time to work and they ultimately fail if skin is re-exposed to the sun's rays. Retin–A® and Renova® (see page 101), skin peels (see page 112) and laser treatments (see page 117) can help. Everyone gets one or two of these, but if you are predisposed to them, be sure you use sunscreen *anytime* you go outside.

Skin Savvy

You can make a refreshing face spritzer by filling a spray mister with mineral water. Store it in the refrigerator to keep it cool then grab it for a quick pick-me-up when your skin feels hot or dry.

Circles Under the Eyes

The skin around the eye is very thin and seems to age before the skin on the rest of our face. In addition to fine lines and wrinkles, bags under the eyes, puffy eyes and circles around the eyes appear as time passes.

Bags under the eyes develop when the fat pads that protect the eyeballs shrink, then work their way past muscles and membranes and lodge just under the skin below the eye. You could diet forever and these fat pads would never disappear. The only solution is to camouflage them with makeup (see page 153) or have the fat removed with lower lid cosmetic surgery.

Puffy Eyes

Puffy eyes come from an accumulation of fluid around the eye. The most common causes for this beauty diminisher include a salty diet, too little or too much sleep, colds, allergy or poor sleep positions. Modifying your diet, elevating your head with pillows when you sleep, avoiding allergens and getting enough sleep help prevent puffy eyes. If you get them, gel filled eye masks that have been chilled can help send the extra fluid in another direction. So can, with careful use, wet tea bags.

Drooping Lids

Droopy eyelids really aren't about droopy lids at all. They have more to do with the folds over the eye, which change when genetics (I got mine from my dad) and the effects of gravity on this tender and thinnest kind of skin play together. Ethel, our makeup expert, became one woman's best friend after she consulted a surgeon who suggested eyelid surgery. Ethel taught her, instead, to use an eye pencil over her upper eye lashes to create a look that made the existing lid look deeper. Camouflage is, indeed, magic.

Fine Lines and Wrinkles

In her book, *I'm Not Getting Older, I'm Getting Better at Denial*, comedian Leigh Anne Jasheway suggests a Sharpei as the ideal pet for women who are aging. She writes: "Looking into the dog's wrinkled face every morning will make your skin seem smooth and firm in comparison."

The laughter this advice generates in a group lends credence to the belief that we are our own worst enemy when it comes to finding a new wrinkle lining our face. Since, in a brainstorming session, you may have heard someone comment positively on a creative idea, "that's a new wrinkle," why, then, is a new wrinkle on our face so undesirable? And where do they come from—especially when they seem to appear overnight?

When you eat protein, it is broken down to amino acids which go into an "amino acid pool." The body draws from this "pool" to recreate different proteins for building and repairing all body tissues. This includes creation of the proteins that produce the body and skin's connective tissues. In the skin, these tissues bind together to form the supportive web of collagen and elastin in the dermis. In time, slower skin turnover, external and internal (mostly self-induced) damage create havoc in the construction process. That supportive edifice begins to crumble. Meantime dehydrated skin cells, poor circulation, shifts in underlying fat and other factors you will learn more about as you delve into this book, contribute to degradation of skin. The end result: WRINKLES.

Sagging Skin

If you have light skin and were exposed to intense sunlight in your younger years, you may discover, later in life, that your face has lots of tough, loose sagging skin that makes you look 15 to 20 years older than your age. The scientific name for this gravity-defying look is solar elastosis.

Excessive exposure to sunlight over many years damages the collagen and elastin fibers, which support your skin. Although makeup can camouflage it to some extent, cosmetic surgery is the only way to lose loose skin. (Read more about this in chapter 17.)

Skin Cancers

Many women are hearing the frightening diagnosis, "This is a skin cancer." Why? Because we live longer and, until recently, we didn't know how damaging the rays of the sun can be. Mix a couple of severe sunburns with time and you get a skin cancer. Dark skin offers only slight protection from skin cancer. Ultraviolet rays are not prejudiced about where they focus their light. There is an entire chapter on sun and another on skin cancer coming soon.

Skin Savvy

Malignant melanoma, the most serious form of skin cancer, is responsible for most deaths from skin cancer.

Skin Tags

They seem to appear out of nowhere—soft, skin-colored growths that hang from your skin on your neck, armpit or groin. Their cause is unknown. You don't have to do anything about them unless they are irritated by clothing. In that case, they can be removed by a dermatologist.

Uneven Skin Texture, Uneven Skin Tone, Dull Appearance

As skin ages the natural exfoliation process by which skin maintains its beauty and condition is reduced. Cells that stay at the surface longer receive more exposure to the environment. This decreased cell turnover results in uneven skin texture, uneven skin tone and a dull appearance.

Section II

When Skin Doesn't Work

"I don't like people who have never fallen or stumbled. Their virtue is lifeless and it isn't of much value. Life hasn't revealed its beauty to them."

Boris Pasternak

6

Skin Damagers

Despite the belief that changes in the skin are due to aging, this is only partially true. With the exception of slower skin regeneration and a slower healing process, skin changes are due to a variety of controllable and uncontrollable factors.

Controllable factors are lifestyle based. For example, there are consequences to alcohol consumption, crash diets and poor exercise habits that affect your skin from the inside out. Externally, exposure to too much sun, pollution or harsh skin care products cause permanent skin damage. Most of the time you are in control of how much exposure you will have to these behaviors. If you want youthful skin you must have the courage to make health and skin fortifying lifestyle change.

You have little choice about the uncontrollable factors that play a role in how your skin changes as you age. For example, you can't change who your parents are, how your body responds to health restoring medication, how often you menstruate or how you body handles temperature. Nevertheless, knowledge is power.

Factors That Control How Skin Changes

Controllable	Uncontrollable
alcohol cigarettes crash diets dehydration diet emotional health exercise habits harsh skin care products pollution sleep deprivation stress sunshine	aging disease facial expression gender genetics (skin texture, ethnicity etc.) gravity hormones injuries photosensitivity reactions

It's Controllable

Alcohol

One of the great pleasures when girlfriends gather is the opportunity to sit down with a glass of water or wine and chat. If your choice is alcohol you may be surprised to learn how it effects your skin.

Alcohol interferes with vitality producing circulation by dilating blood vessels. It depletes the body of vitamins and minerals necessary for skin cell life. It dehydrates skin. All this causes skin to be puffy and blotchy and interferes with healthy cell regeneration. Need I say more?

If you want healthy skin (think complexion), minimize your alcohol intake. Make one or two drinks (wine, mixed drinks or beer) your limit. Alternate each with a glass of water.

> If you drink too much alcohol the toll on the liver will show on the skin. It gets sallow. Over time alcohol causes the dilation of blood vessels, which create a "blush" effect on pores of the nose and cheeks. The pores become enlarged. This is not a pretty picture.

> ## Nutrition Savvy
> Alcohol and beverages that contain caffeine dehydrate your system. Because maintaining the homeostasis of the internal organs is of prime importance, the skin is often the first to suffer.

Cigarettes

When I was young, magazine ads led us to believe that smoking was glamorous. Movies featured beautiful women clasping elegant wands that held long cigarettes with smoke curling seductively from the end. Cigarettes gave us something to do with our hands and people who smoked them took pride in their ability to inhale deeply then blow smoke rings.

As little as ten years ago, smoking was still cool. The Surgeon General told us that smoking was bad for our health but there were still ashtrays on restaurant tables and circular sand-filled bins in front of elevator doors in department stores and doctor's offices. You could smoke on an airplane.

My how times have changed! Tobacco companies admit they added addiction-producing nicotine to cigarettes. Many states have made it unlawful to smoke in public places. Although there are still mini-ashtrays on the arms of airplane seats and in their lavatories, if you light up you will set off alarms and be evicted at the next stop. People who smoke at work must do it outside the building. Smoke one pack of cigarettes a day for twenty years and it is almost certain you will get lung cancer.

If you smoke, you have ample warning about what cigarettes will do to your lungs, but too little information about what they do to your face. Puffing on these little sticks of dynamite causes a puckering of lips as muscles contract repeatedly while the user draws on the cigarette. Heat, nicotine and smoke damages elastin and collagen and causes changes in the blood vessels that supply the oxygen necessary for cell turnover. The result is fine, feathery lines around the lip area that even a skilled surgeon can't remove.

Smokers get wrinkles long before their non-smoking friends. Non-smokers who hang out with smokers get wrinkles long before people who avoid inhaling second hand smoke.

If you smoke, stop. I agree it is easier said than done, but there are excellent programs and product to support withdrawal from this skin-damaging habit that is second only to the sun for the damage it causes.

If you don't smoke, don't start. Don't hang out with smokers. It isn't cool. It is deadly. You'll regret it each time you look in the mirror.

Crash Diets

Crash diets *don't* work. There are many reasons why they don't work but a few specifically affect your skin suit.

Skin stretches. If you've gained weight or had a baby you know how remarkable that feature is. It also can shrink back to its original size. How easily it does that is based on genetics and the condition of your skin. When it comes to measuring what a women sees in the mirror, most women focus on their abdomen and thighs but when you gain weight you gain it all over. When you lose it, it may appear to come off in only one place but it is being "lost" from all over your body.

That means that skin on your face is also impacted by changes in weight, especially yo-yo dieting that causes skin to stretch then (hopefully) shrink many times. As the underlying supportive connective tissue gets weaker it contributes to "saggy" skin and the wrinkles that causes. The best thing you can do for your beautiful self is to get to a weight you can maintain for a long time.

Dehydration

The father of medicine, Hippocrates, preached the benefits of using water. Every diet, skin care and exercise book urges us to drink at least 8 glasses of water a day. Anything that removes water from your body and your environment is harmful to your skin because your body will look to skin last when it is meeting its fluid needs. Chapter 26, on water, will flush (if you'll excuse the pun) this out further.

Nutrition Savvy
Thirst equals dehydration over the entire body but it shows first on your skin. For healthy skin, prevent and quench thirst with water.

Diet

You may be surprised to learn that your diet can have a significant effect on your skin. Eat a lot of carrots and your skin will turn orange. Avoid all fats and oils and your skin will be dry. Avoid carbohydrates (fruits and vegetables) and you'll set yourself up for an internal attack of cell damaging free radicals.

For more on the intricacies of a healthy skin suit diet, see Chapter 24.

Emotional Health

In the introduction to this book I wrote that when I was a dispensing pharmacist I discovered many of the prescriptions I filled were for patients whose emotional problems were manifested in a variety of skin dis-eases. When queried, my doctor friends expressed wonder at the frequency with which medical conditions, including those of the skin, appeared and disappeared as their patient's psychological states changed.

When you can't express your feelings and emotions appropriately or make logical sense of what's happening in your life, those unprocessed experiences move from the cognitive centers of your brain into your body. Ever noticed how someone who is angry gets red in the face or experiences a rash around their neck and chest? This is about more than the emotion itself.

Since women who get angry or cry are still described as "too emotional," or worse, it takes courage to stand our ground when we get mad, sad or glad. Good skin health demands that we learn to dig our heels in productively rather than dig our fingernails into our skin. Our beauty depends on it.

Stress Reduction Savvy
You can help prevent "expression lines" in your face by taking time to "relax" from the tensions of the day.

Exercise Habits

When we think exercise we usually think about what it does to our weight, our heart, our lungs and our stamina. We rarely think "skin" although exercise is a primary factor in keeping skin healthy because it improves circulation and generates new capillaries, which can deliver oxygen rich blood and nutrients to skin.

The role of exercise ranks so high on the list of information you can use for skin health there's an entire chapter about it beginning on page 167.

Harsh Skin Care Products and Other Chemicals

Just because a product is easily attainable doesn't mean it is safe. Skin is alive. If you use an irritable product you will quickly learn, via the feedback from your skin's nerve cells, that the product isn't good for you. Your skin will get red, swollen, itch or blister. Common sense must prevail.

Skin Savvy
Waterproof kitchen gloves provide protection from detergents and the hot and cold water you use to wash dishes. They can also prevent the skin on your hands from breathing and trap perspiration. If you plan to wear gloves for a long time, remove them every 15 minutes or so to let the skin on your hands "breathe".

Pollution

Your skin is regularly assaulted with pollution. Although skin is a barrier that prevents smoke, car exhausts, factory emissions and other pollutants from invading the deep layers of the skin, they create visible and invisible damage. Damage to external and internal body surfaces are impacted by the free radicals these agents produce. Inside, they set the stage for disease. From the outside they attack the genetic material that is essential to reproduction of new skin cells as well as skin repair mechanisms. They react with protein in the cell's collagen resulting in a loss of skin elasticity. Now we know mother was wise when she said, "Eat your vegetables." The antioxidants they (and fruits) contain can neutralize these free radicals and stem the tide of dis-ease. We are just learning about the effectiveness of these same nutrients when applied externally. You will learn more about this in Chapter 14.

You can avoid some pollution by staying away from people who smoke and environments where other agents are concentrated. Protect your skin with long sleeves and use rubber gloves when it is time to use cleaning products.

This is called "clean living."

Sleep Deprivation

Moms don't need the results of double-blinded research to dispense wise advice. They reminded us it was bedtime by saying, "Time for your beauty sleep," without knowing that it is during sleep that your energy levels are restored, tissue repair is at its height and your skin's rate of cell renewal can cook at high speed.

Since these important biochemical and physiological processes take place while we sleep, it makes little sense to me when I hear someone say we need less sleep as we age. I know that when I am deprived of sleep I feel it internally and see it externally. Nevertheless, the amount of time we spend sleeping has decreased an average of two hours a night in the last century.

The downside of sleep is the horizontal sleep position that prevents gravity from sending body fluids south of your face. Alcohol, salty food, allergies and pre-menstrual fluid retention are just a few of the reasons you can awaken looking like a puff adder even when you get enough sleep. (See page 35—puffy eyes)

When I was young, an elderly neighbor told me that to get rid of occasional morning puffiness (caused by fluid retention) she used the tea bags from her morning tea. She rested for 15 minutes on her back, towel under her head, with the now cool, wet tea bags over her closed eyes. My neighbor didn't know that teas contain alkaloids and polyphenols which are soothing to swollen tissue. (See antioxidants on page 101 to learn more about the role of tea for skin health.) Another home remedy women swear by uses a 1/4-inch slice of cucumber the same way.

If you have a chronically ill child, sleep apnea or a job that deprives you of restorative sleep, catnaps can keep you from running on empty. If you don't fall asleep easily, sleep deeply enough, or get enough sleep, attempt to create a routine that incorporates relaxation and good skin care. Begin a bath-before-bed habit. Keep your window open to expose your skin and lungs to higher levels of body-relaxing oxygen. Don't eat late unless your meal includes lots of nutrient rich, good-for-the-face fruits and vegetables. Experiment to find out if white noise, soft music, a dim light or a special pillow can lull you to slumber land without medication. Your skin will love you for it.

Sleep Savvy

Your sleep position will determine whether the skin on your face looks rested, smooshed or stretched during sleep because of the pressure applied at pillow points for long periods of time. Skin specialists recommend developing the habit of sleeping on your back with your head slightly elevated. Good surgeons demand it for several weeks after any cosmetic procedure. (Think La-Z-Boy.) It may take some time before you can sleep this way, but your face will thank you for it.

Her Story

When I was in college I got by on five hours sleep a night. I also cultivated one of the most useful habits I have today—a catnap. Later I learned to sleep sitting up. Several months ago, I was visiting my daughter. She left me in the car while she delivered something to a client. The "drop off" took longer than usual. She entered the car somewhat abashed until she realized I'd been asleep. "I forgot you can fall asleep anywhere, anytime," she said. "That's it!" she said. "No more worrying about keeping you waiting."

Eight Girlfriends Suggest Remedies for Sleeplessness

✓ Take a warm bath, towel off and dive under a quilt.
✓ Read a magazine and fall asleep with the light on.
✓ Ask your hubby to snuggle.
✓ Pet a pet.
✓ Milk and a cookie has worked for me for forty years.
✓ Write about your day in a gratitude journal.
✓ Turn off all the lights except a nightlight. Turn on a soothing CD.
✓ Try yoga or another breath oriented relaxation process.

Stress

Despite its bad reputation, we couldn't live without some stress in our lives. Sadly, too many of us have too much for too long. More than anything else, stress contributes to unhealthy habits including smoking, drinking, poor eating habits, failure to exercise and poor sleep patterns. It also triggers the body to produce surging then receding fight or flight hormones which, over time, can cause skin problems. You may be surprised to learn that the most significant contributing factor to acne is not chocolate, fried foods or your menstrual cycle. It is stress.

If you have stress you are experiencing dis-ease. If you want good looking skin, find a healthy way to defuse stress. Then, make a plan to re-direct your life so your skin and your body can remain disease-free.

Consider also trying some of the skin indulgences on page 129. When they de-stress your skin they will also de-stress your mind and body.

Sunshine

Every book or internet site about skin care has at least one section devoted to the damage sun does to the skin. This damage is called photoaging. Whole industries are built around products to prevent and remedy sun damage caused when ultraviolet rays of the sun speed destruction of collagen and elastin and produce a leathery skin texture not seen in "normal" aging. Sun exposure is, without doubt, the number one reason we get crow's feet, blotchy blood vessels, thin skin, brown spots, furrowing and wrinkles. Suffice it to say, in short, that you should, at all costs, avoid the sun if you want to avoid the havoc it can create on your skin.

Chapter 9 of this book is devoted to learning more about this devastating beauty destroyer.

> Photoaging is a medical term for skin damage caused by exposure to ultraviolet (UV) rays of the sun.

8

It's Uncontrollable: Aging

Although a healthy diet, regular exercise, plenty of sleep and stress management help, the blessings of greeting another day is tempered, on our skin, by the biological aging that occurs without sun damage. Skin cells get more dehydrated and skin gets thinner with age. Our sweat glands produce less sweat, our sebaceous glands produce less oil and circulation can become impaired. Muscles and fat shift (south). No skin treatment can make cells regenerate the way they did when we were young.

Aging means grieving *and* celebrating the loss of youthful experiences. While we are busy focusing on fine lines that become deep fissures and settling skin that becomes jowls we must also focus on our opportunities to live in the present instead of the past. Now is the time to realize that perfection is impossible, imperfection is human, the only person we can change is our self and the solution to life's dilemmas, including how we will or won't let our skin affect our life, lies within.

Disease

Although the way we live can prevent many of the diseases that come our way, we are not in control of some of the larger events of our life that play themselves out on our skin.

The list of diseases that show up as skin symptoms is lengthy and the side effects of diseases over which we have no control is also lengthy. Dermatologists, the doctors who diagnose and treat diseases of the skin, talk about macules, papules, nodules, cysts, scales, rosacea and purpura as well as specific diseases that manifest themselves on the skin including acne, psoriasis, vitiligo, warts, impetigo, poison ivy, herpes and the "big C" word, cancer.

If you have any changes on your skin at any time, call your doctor. **Your beauty, outside and in, depends on it.**

Facial Expressions

Facial expressions get etched on our face when we, unconsciously, contract small muscles over and over again as we react and respond to life events. These can contribute to the best kind of wrinkle. Laugh lines mean we've laughed. Horizontal lines between the eyebrows are a demonstration of our curiosity and horizontal forehead lines can be an expression of a delight-filled life. The downside is that squinting can cause crow's feet, grimacing can cause pursed lips and that right eyebrow we trained ourselves to raise is higher than the left one.

Women often attach skin tape to those areas where their facial expressions are contributing to unwanted wrinkles. Then, when muscles are contracted, the pull against the tape reminds us to relax the muscles contributing to a lined face. The system can work with superficial expression lines but it usually takes face peels, filler injections, dermabrasion or cosmetic surgery to undo deeper creases. Fair warning in advance: these wrinkle removal techniques provide only temporary relief if you don't change your habits.

When we look at elders with deep wrinkles caused by facial expressions we admirably call them character lines. No one can deny the creativity of an entertainer or actor with a face that says more by its expression than it does with words. Think Lucille Ball.

Gender

We're women. We don't have as much testosterone as men. That's why we don't have as much hair. Our skin isn't as tough or as thick as our male friends. That is why we show the effects of damage more quickly. Need I say more?

Genetics (Heredity)

You have your father's jowls, your mother's creamy complexion, your aunt's dry skin or your grandmother's imperfectly shaped lips. Genetics is about heredity. How you look, under your makeup, has a lot to do with the package you are given at birth. For example, everyone is born with the same number of melanocytes. It is the amount and concentration of the melanin, a factor of your genetic make up, that determines how dark or light your skin will be.

Gravity

Scientists spend a lot of effort studying astronauts in an attempt to determine what effect a gravity-free environment has on their bodies. Perhaps, in time, we will learn if a prolonged gravity-free life prevents droopy eyelids, under-eye fat deposits, facial folds and the lengthening nose that are the inevitable consequences of living where the earth exerts a downward pull on our body.

Hormone Shifts

Some evidence exists that hormone- or estrogen-replacement therapy in postmenopausal women may help prevent skin slackness, although it does not seem to affect elasticity. One study reported that estrogen therapy reduced wrinkles, although many experts questioned the methods used in the study and advised women who want to take estrogen to do so because of its other health benefits, not for wrinkle-prevention. Wise women know that their skin changes from day to day and is oilier or dryer before, during and after their menstrual period. They believe that it has to be more than a coincidence that after menopause everything changes. Despite the proven knowledge that most uncontrollable skin changes are about gender, genetics and sun exposure, those of us who know how little research has been conducted on the relationship between surging and diminishing hormones and women's skin believe science will prove later what we already know.

Injuries

Cuts, bumps and lumps, burns and bruises are an inevitable part of life. Sometimes these injuries heal quickly and sometimes they are severe enough to cause scarring.

R.I.C.E. is an acronym for the rest, ice, compression and elevation that can decrease swelling and internal bleeding after an injury. Once an injury has occurred, a combination of medical and wise women wisdom for healing is synergized by good nutrition practices that assure you get the nutrients your body mobilizes in the calorie burning process called healing.

Photosensitivity

Every summer since I've known her, my friend, Kitty, has developed a dark tan. Despite hours in the sun as a tennis player, then a college tennis coach, she never sunburned. Four years ago she attended her first Speaking of Women's Health conference and learned the importance of tempering that dark tan. Now educated, she uses SPF 30, wears a hat, sunglasses and protective clothing during those inevitable lengthy outside coaching hours.

Last year Kitty developed a chest infection prior to an important tournament. Her doctor prescribed an antibiotic. The label on her prescription bottle warned the drug could increase photosensitivity so Kitty added a darker pair of sunglasses to her usual pre-sunning routine. But, midday, she realized she'd suffered a severe sunburn. She thought photo-sensitivity was about eyes. It is not.

> Drugs that help often (also) harm.

Photosensitivity or photo-toxicity is the name given to a skin reaction caused when certain drugs (including popular herbal supplements) make your skin super sensitive to the ultra-violet rays from the sun or another source. These photo-reactive agents, like Kitty's antibiotic, can cause everything from mild allergic reactions, to hives, eczema-like rashes and the red, swelling and sometimes blistering and oozing caused by sunburn. (See the lists that begin on page 60.).

Sun Savvy
There is no known safe way to tan. A suntan is the skin's response to injury.

There are other products that cause photosensitive *and* photo-allergic reactions to the skin in some people but not others. These trigger your immune system and cause an itchy rash. The most common culprits are deodorants, antibacterial soaps, nylon and wool fibers, mothballs, chemicals injected into the skin during tattooing and fragrances in skin care products.

Any agent that removes the top layers of our skin make it exceptionally susceptible to damage from other agents, including the sun. Be sure to check the label of every product you purchase to see if it carries the photosensitivity warning.

Not everyone who uses medications or products containing photo-reactive agents will have a photo-reaction. On the other hand, people who are allergic to one chemical may develop photosensitivity to another.

If you are taking medications that are photosensitive, you should:

1. Avoid the sun between the hours of 10 a.m. and 3 p.m.
2. Liberally apply a sunscreen—preferably one containing a total sun block such as zinc oxide or titanium dioxide. (Be sure to reapply after swimming or any activity that produces sweating.)
3. Avoid sunscreens that are scented or sunscreens containing PABA.
4. Wear protective clothing, including a broad-brimmed hat and sunglasses that protect against UV rays.

Skin Savvy

Fair skinned people are usually more susceptible to photosensitivity but it is not uncommon for a black skinned or dark tanned person, like Kitty, to have a reaction.

If you have any change in products you use, are prescribed a new medication or choose to use one of the many over-the-counter products, including herbal supplements, don't spend a lot of time in the sun until you are sure that it won't make you more miserable than the problem it was meant to cure.

If you have a photosensitive reaction:

1. Treat it as you would a sunburn.
2. Take a cool bath or shower and use over-the-counter pain relievers (follow label directions).
3. Inform your doctor about your reaction.
4. For severe reactions, prescription medications may help ease symptoms.

Drugs and Chemicals That Can Cause Photosensitive Reactions

Note: The product list that follows is not conclusive. Be sure to check with your pharmacist regarding the photosensitivity potential of any prescription, over-the-counter-medication, herbal supplement or vitamin you take.

Drug Class	Some Examples
Acne Treatments	Isotretinoin (Accutane®, Avita®, Vesanoid®)
Anti-wrinkle Creams	Renova®
Anti-microbials (Antibiotics, Anti-fungals, Sulfa Drugs)	Tetracycline (many brand names) Griseofulvin (Fulvicin®, Grisactin®,Grifulvin®) Sulfa Based (Azulfidine®, Bactrim,® Sulfasala®, Sulfasalazine®)
Anti-Depressants	St. John's Wort, Desipramine (Norpramin®) Methotrimeprazine (Nozinan®) Sertraline (Zoloft®) Trazadone (Desyrel®) Tricyclic derivatives (Elavil®, Aventy®1, Pamelor®)
Cancer Treatment Drugs	Dacarbazine Doxorubicin HCl (Doxol®) 5-fluorocytosine Fluorouracil Methotrexate Vinblastine
Cardiac and Anti-Hypertensive Drugs	Dyazide® Maxside®

Drug Class	Some Examples
Nonsteroidal Anti-inflammatory Drugs (NSAIDs)	Aspirin Ibuprofen Naproxen
Oral Hypoglycemics	Glucotrol® Micronase
Sulfa Based Drugs	Bactrim®
Thiazide Diuretics	Lasix® Diuril® Hydrodiuril®
Herbal Products	St. John's Wort
Other Products	
Perfumes and Bar Soaps	Contain quinoline, musk ambrette, 6-methyl-coumarin, bergamot oil and sandalwood oil.
After Shave Lotions	
Dandruff Shampoos That Contain Coal Tar Ingredients	
Skin Bleaching Creams	
Sunscreens	Anything with Para-aminobenzoic acid (PABA)

9

Sun Sense

The idea that earth is threatened by life from outer space has been the source of inspiration for radio and television shows, movies, books and bedtime stories for years. In fact, earth is being bombarded at all times and running for cover is a good idea.

Surprisingly, the threat isn't visible. Yes, the sun is the source, but the harm is not from its visible light rays. It is the invisible ultraviolet rays, also produced by the sun's light, that trigger the changes in skin that give us a tan, sunburn, blisters, wrinkles and sagging skin. It is an awful consequence considering how wonderful the warmth of the sun's rays feel on our skin.

There are three kinds of damaging ultraviolet rays: ultraviolet A (UVA), ultraviolet B (UVB) and ultraviolet C (UVC). Although all three can damage skin, only UVA and UVB rays penetrate the ozone layer of the earth.

Skin Biochemistry 101

When ultraviolet rays hit the skin, the melanocyte cells in the basal layer of your epidermis spring into action. Everyone is born with the same number of melanocytes, but your ethnic background determines how much melanin is concentrated inside them.

If your ancestors lived in parts of the world where the sun was intense you have lots of melanin and the color of your skin ranges from easy-to-tan olive to almost black. You can be somewhat carefree when you are in the sun because you don't burn easily. If your ancestors lived in parts of the world where there was cold weather and cloud cover you have a low concentration of melanin and your skin is fair and freckled. You probably learned early in life that if you were in the sun very long you would pay for that exposure with a sunburn.

Sun Savvy

Even on a cloudy day, eighty percent of the sun's ultraviolet rays pass through the clouds.

Sun Now, Pay Later

Regardless of your skin color, your skin was not designed to have the long, unprotected exposure that too many of us have given to our skin. As you gardened in the hot sun, took walks by the seashore, hiked and skied in the mountains and intentionally sat in the sun to feel the sun's comforting warm rays, (often seeking the tan we believed made skin look healthy, vibrant and radiant,) those invisible UVA and UVB rays were wreaking havoc on the uncovered parts of your skin. The length and strength of the rays and how much of their power could be blocked by the keratin of your skin determined where the damage was done. If they get by the keratin (UVA rays are better at that) their damage is primarily to the dermis and the elastin and fibrin that keeps skin from sagging. The rays that didn't get by (UVB rays) were content to damage the epidermis, causing wrinkles. Both were stimulating the melanin in the melanocytes, darkening the pigment of your skin to give added protection from this damage. Although you may read that UVA causes aging and UVB causes burning, each do both.

UVA Rays	UVB Rays
✓ greater in number	✓ shorter, fewer in number
✓ less intense	✓ more intense
✓ 20% absorbed by skin keratin	✓ 60% absorbed by skin keratin
✓ longer to penetrate deeper layers of skin	✓ shorter to attack top layer of skin
✓ attack elastin and fibrin causing wrinkles and sagging	✓ cause sunburn and wrinkles
✓ destroy protective skin antibodies	✓ more dangerous for skin cancer
✓ penetrate water to 3 feet	✓ penetrate water to 3 feet

If you look at the skin of *dark-skinned* elderly women it becomes easy to see that the concentration of melanin has protected them somewhat from these damaging rays. Their skin is void of wrinkles. Compared to light- skinned women the same age, they look twenty years younger. But, regardless of skin color, no one is immune to the cell changes produced by the sun's rays. That's why everyone born since our lifespan lengthened has a risk of skin cancer. (You will learn more about this in the next chapter.)

Sun Savvy
Fog, smog and clouds do not provide an adequate block to the sun's harmful UV rays. Up to 80% of UV light penetrates on overcast days.

A Gift for Our Children

Several years ago, experts estimated that eighty percent of our lifetime sun exposure occurs before the age of twenty. That may be tempered recently by the sadly less active life of children who spend too much time inside in front of the television and computers. Nevertheless, any unprotected sun exposure, especially when we are young, is the greatest cause of wrinkles, sagging skin, deadly melanoma and other skin cancers later in life. There are many gifts we can give ourselves and our children to support a healthy later life. Skin protection is one them.

Sunscreen History

In the late fifties we not only didn't protect our skin, we used oils, lotions and creams believing we were enhancing a tan. By the late sixties, commercial products called suntan creams were on the market. In the seventies the first products designed to prevent sunburn were introduced. The magic ingredient was Para-Aminobenzoic Acid (PABA) designed to block the UVB rays most responsible for tanning. PABA, a chemical, stained clothes and irritated the skin of many people who used it, so researchers looked for other products to protect us from sunburn. In the eighties, dermatologists, seeing a dramatic increase in skin cancers, alerted us to the death threat of too much sun. By the nineties, scientists told us that UVA rays, as well as UVB rays, were also damaging. This information precipitated warnings to stay out of the sun, especially at midday, during hot seasons and while at high altitudes. Thus, products that blocked both rays of the sun, rather than products to enhance the effects of the sun, became the focus of sun savvy marketing. We can buy sunscreens, which absorb the sun's rays or sun blocks that work by scattering or reflecting damaging rays.

ABCs of SPFs

Sun protection may be the most vital part of skin care. Avoiding the sun in the hottest part of the day is common sense. But habits change slowly and the reality is that many women continue to struggle with a desire to have some sun-induced skin color without wrinkles or cancer. As a result we wrestle with SPF numbers hoping to arrive at the perfect numerical equation for a "safe" tan.

SPF is the abbreviation for Sun Protection Factor. This number gives you some indication of how long you can stay in the sun without suffering the effects of (only) UVB's burning rays. The *theory* works this way:

Suppose you can be in the sun fifteen minutes without damage from the sun's burning UVB rays. If you use a product with an SPF of 6 it means you can stay in the sun six times longer without getting burned. (15 x 6 = 90 minutes or 1.5 hours) An SPF of 10 would give you protection of 15 x 10 or 150 minutes which translates into 2.5 hours.

Theories are great but when it comes to sun, it isn't that simple. In the reality of science the increase in number is not proportionate to the protection. For example, an SPF of 15 blocks out 93 percent of harmful rays and an SPF of 30 about 97 percent. However, there are many more variables that play a role in how quickly sun damage begins. They include the time of day, the altitude, whether you are near water, whether you reapply after swimming or sweating or putting on then removing clothing. The biggest variable is how much product we use. Most users apply only fifty percent of the recommended amount so they receive only 50% of the SPF protection the product offers. In other words, if you apply just a small amount of an SPF 30 sunscreen, you'll only get the protection of an SPF 15.

Variables that Affect SPF Factors

✓ time of day
✓ altitude
✓ proximity to water, sand and/or snow
✓ swimming
✓ sweating
✓ how often you apply and reapply sunscreen

Sunscreen products offer a range of protection that begins at 2 and goes as high as 60. Since there is no international standard, a product that is SPF 30 in the U. S. may only be equivalent to an SPF 10 purchased in another country. Every dermatologist I talked to believed a product with an SPF of less than 15 was useless and one with more than SPF 30 didn't add that much more protection. They also added the advice to apply it every day (even when it is cloudy) 15 minutes before you go outside, and reapply it often.

Warning

The SPF in sunscreens account for protecting only the UVB tanning rays. There is no rating system for UVA protection. To prevent skin damage always look for "broad spectrum UVA/UVB protection."

Sun Savvy
The chemicals in sunscreens can be irritating to skin. If you have sensitive skin, a sun block is a wiser choice for protection from the sun.

What's in Those Products?

My research revealed there are more than 60 sunscreen agents in more than 120 products including creams, gels, lip balms, lotions oils, and sticks. According to Dr. Henry W. Lim, chairman of the Department of Dermatology at the Henry Ford Health System in Detroit, avobenzone (Parsol 1789) "is the best UVA protection on the market in the U.S."

Zinc oxide and titanium dioxide offer another form of UVA protection by physically deflecting the rays. It's the same thick white stuff lifeguards used to use, but now it's available in a microfine, almost-clear form. Dr. Lim says that it doesn't absorb as well as avobenzone or some other products, but it does offer significant protection and it is thought to be safer for small children and people who have allergic reactions to many sunscreens.

More than You Need to Know?

Meantime, the PABA that was discarded years ago has been refined and the newer "esters" rarely stain clothing. There are other chemicals including benzophenones (oxybenzone), cinnamates (octylmethyl cinnamate and cinoxate) and salicylates that work on UVB rays and benzophenones (oxybenzone, sulisobenzone, titanium dioxide, zinc oxide, and avobenzone) to protect you from UVA rays.

Like most products we put on our skin we make purchases based on an aesthetic as well as a functional use. Packaging may be important to one person and how it feels on the skin or what it smells like makes it a "best buy" for another. **Regardless of what you look for when you shop for a sunscreen always look for broad spectrum UVA/UVB protection and remember: what you pay for a product has nothing to do with its effectiveness.**

Sunscreen Savvy

Sunscreen ingredients can cause allergic skin reactions. Before you lather your skin with sunburn protection, be sure to test the product on the inside of your arm just above the elbow. If it doesn't cause a reaction there it is probably safe to use.

When You Must Get Color: Self Tanning

Now the golden days of sun worship are over and tanning is a beauty faux pas. Ideally, everyone, regardless of color, should feel comfortable with the shade of skin they were born with. Since that isn't the reality, there is an alternative. Self-tanners are the fastest-growing segment of the sun-care industry. Best of all they work better than ever without making your skin turn orange.

All sunless tanners work the same way. They contain dihydroxyacetone (DHA), which reacts with the amino acids in your skin to produce a darkened color. This reaction takes place in the uppermost layers of the skin, which sloughs off quickly, so self tan products will last no longer than a week. If you use a self tanner, do it this way:

1. Wash and exfoliate the skin to leave a smooth surface for the tan to develop.
2. Moisturizers and sun screens interfere with the DHA reaction. If you like moisturizers, buy self-tanners with a moisturizing base.
3. Use long, even strokes to apply the product. Don't forget the "hidden" spots on the back of your neck, under your arms, inside your thighs an the back of your knees.
4. Wash your hands after using to prevent an uneven deposit there.
5. Stay out of water for at least an hour.

Self-tanners work on the top, easy to slough off layers of skin so don't expect a product to last more than a week. Although some products claim to offer sun protection my dermatology docs say, "You *must* use at least an SPF 15 whenever you go outside."

The Final Answer

There may, in time, be ways to protect and repair your skin from sun exposure but a woman who says, "Oh, well, the damage is done. I might as well ignore all of these sun warnings," is in denial. If you want your skin to look like a million dollars, the best thing you can do for it is to stay out of the sun. Before you ask any more questions, that is my final answer.

10

Skin Cancer

Her Story

    The first seventeen years of my life were spent growing up in the mountains (altitude, 2200 feet) of Western North Carolina. One of my favorite sunny *day pastimes was jumping on my bicycle and pumping to the top of the mountain behind my home where I could lay in isolation, watching sunbeams dance on the horizon. Later I spent four years seeking the sun (with reflectors) in the courtyard behind my college dormitory. I got married and soon found myself living in Denver, CO (altitude 5,000 feet). In time, my family and I settled in the Pacific Northwest where, with the exception of one year near Lake Tahoe, CA (altitude 7,500 feet), I enjoyed relief from shoveling snow and scraping ice off car windows. Then I began spending as much of the winter season as possible in the mountains of Arizona where being in the sun is a way of life.*

    Because I was aware that my "tan" lifestyle had a dark side, I have always been vigilant about examining my skin. Sure enough, about ten years ago, I noticed a red spot on the fleshy part of my cheek that seemed to fade and then get red again. I went to a surgeon who quickly diagnosed it as a basal cell cancer which, she reported, could be easily excised. I agreed, succumbed to the novocaine and let her have at it. When the "procedure" was over I was stunned to learn that she'd used 18 internal and external stitches to repair the damage. I was grateful but mortified at the prospect of a visible scar on a complexion that was finally blemish free. Happily, her steady hand and superb skills resulted in a recovery that requires an eagle eye to see where her incision was made. Nevertheless, the experience was an eye opener that precipitated a change in my sunning habits.

Sun Savvy

Just three blistering burns in your teenage years can increase the risk of skin cancer up to twenty years after the original exposure.

Skin Cancer 101

If you have been in the sun for any length of time, had a severe or blistering sunburn, spent time in tanning beds, live at higher elevations or in the Sun Belt (southern U. S.) you have an increased risk for skin cancer. Other risk factors include fair skin, light blue or green eyes and a family history for any kind of skin growth.

Skin cancers get their name based on the cells from which they originate. Basically there are three types including (in increasing degree of severity):

Basal cell skin cancer originates in the basal cells of the epidermis. They are the most benign, but most prevalent, skin cancer. They are common after age forty, especially if you have fair skin. They usually appear on your face, ears, neck, chest or back as a waxy or pearly bump or a flat, pink, scar-like growth. Most people who have one get another within five years. Basal cell skin cancers are diagnosed by scraping a piece of skin (a biopsy) for examination under a microscope. They are treated with topical medications or minor surgery and almost never spread. That is why, with early detection, they are almost always curable.

Squamous cell skin cancer originates in the squamous cells of the lower layers of the epidermis. They are more common after age fifty, especially if you have fair skin. They usually appear on your face, ears, neck, hands or arms as firm, red, bumps or flat, scaly and crusty growths. They have a greater potential for malignancy, but with early detection, they, too, are almost always curable.

Word Savvy

The word malignant comes from the Latin translation "acting maliciously." In medical language it means the disease has a tendency to become progressively worse.

Melanoma, the most serious skin cancer, rears its ugly head from those melanocyte skin cells that are responsible for the pigment of your skin. They can develop anywhere on your body and have a variety of appearances. A growth that changes or is associated with itching or an abnormal feeling in that area of your skin can be a melanoma. So can small growths with irregular borders and red, white, blue or black spots.

Because we are blessed with a longer life, it's estimated that one in 75 Americans will be diagnosed with melanoma before they die. The risk of developing a melanoma doubles every ten years. If treated early it is usually curable. But, once it spreads to your lymph nodes or other organs survival rates remain grim.

There are five basic warning signs of the most common types of skin cancer that *require* a visit to your doctor:

✓ an open sore that does not heal after three weeks
✓ a persistent, painful or itchy reddened area that crusts over from time to time
✓ a smooth growth with a raised edge
✓ a pearly or semi-transparent red, white, pink, brown or black mole-like nodule
✓ a white or yellow scar-like area

Warning Signs of Skin Cancer

- A sore that appears, heals, and reappears
- A mole or any spot that begins to itch or bleed
- A new mole
- A mole that changes texture, color, shape or size

A Warning

Pollution is thinning the protective ozone layer that surrounds the earth. As a result, doctors are diagnosing an increased number of skin cancer in patients in their twenties and thirties.

Breast Self-Exam and Skin Scan

Unless you have been living in a cave, you know that a monthly breast self-exam should be part of your personal health care routine. You may not know how important it is to add a skin scan to that routine to look for signs of skin cancer. You are looking for abnormalities including new moles and changes in old ones. Here's how:

✓ Use a mirror to look at your naked body, both front and back, then right and left sides with arms raised.

✓ Lift any hair on the back of your head and use a hand mirror to examine the back of the scalp and neck.

✓ Check your back and buttocks with a hand mirror.

✓ Bend your elbows and look carefully at forearms, upper underarms and palms.

✓ Look at the backs of the legs and feet, including soles and the spaces between your toes.

If you live with someone, share a skin exam to be sure you look at places you may be unable to see. If you live alone, be sure to ask a trusted friend or health professional to do this with and for you. Cancer prevention *is* a thing of beauty.

Sun Savvy

The incidence of skin cancer has increased significantly in Australia where the ozone layer that protects earth from the sun's rays is thinnest.

11

Skin Breakouts

Her Story

When I was a teen my sebaceous glands put in so much overtime I could run my index finger along the side of my nose and use the "grease" to massage my cuticles. That oily texture, and the genes that gave me an olive complexion, contributed to a natural resistance to sunburn and, later, few wrinkles compared to other women my age. The downside was acne flare-ups. I believed that aggressive scrubbing would clear my skin. Now I know I only irritated it and made it crank out more oil.

Happily these flare-ups decreased as I aged, but about the time I'd think my blemished skin was a thing of the past a new pimple would erupt. Until I was fifty, I often delivered a self-deprecating comment that I was doomed to die with a zit in the center of my forehead.

Now my skin care regimen and professionally administered facials have limited breakouts to an occasional whitehead, which I can always link to stress and, probably, the slightly depressed immune system that goes with it. Instead of the poking that damaged my young skin, I opt for a mild anti-bacterial cream and patience.

Skin savvy is a good thing.

Life Is a Joke

When your reach that time in life when you begin coping with fine lines and wrinkles, the appearance of a skin blemish can seem like nature's cruelest joke. Nevertheless, despite the fact that complexions get drier (and less susceptible to blemishes) as we age, scrutiny of the face often reveals a blemish.

Although there are many diseases of the skin, including several that manifest themselves on the face (rosacea and lupus are the most common), most women continue to experience transient skin problems throughout their life. The best course of action when you see something different on your face is to make friends with a dermatologist. When it comes to simple blemishes, however, there is good news. Read on.

Acne — It's the Pits

Acne is the official name for what most of us call "zits." It is the result of an accumulation of excess oil (sebum) in skin pores and hair follicles. The oil closes off this "environment" encouraging inflammation-causing bacteria to thrive. The bacteria continue to grow, infection occurs and soon you have a pimple.

Teen acne is primarily the result of hormonal changes, which stimulate the sebaceous glands of the skin. When we mature we continue to have fluctuating sexual hormones that cause skin changes. Stress, and the hormones it precipitates, seems to be the prime culprit when it comes to adult breakouts. Oily hair products that get into your pores when your hair touches your face, perspiration that doesn't get rinsed off after a workout and some medications that help other parts of your body can cause acne.

If, as a youngster, you were told that keeping your face clean would prevent acne, you may still be living with that misconception. Scrubbing only stimulates the skin to produce more oil, supporting that sebum accumulation that acne-causing bacteria love. Instead, the strategy you can use to avoid acne is based on your skin texture.

For Dry Skin

Use a mild cleanser once or twice a day. You can safely apply an antibiotic cream on the blemishes, but should avoid layering on other rich, greasy products that may combat dryness but will support additional breakouts.

For Normal To Oily Skin

Use a mild cleanser and exfoliate. Use creams with salicylic acid or benzoyl peroxide. Mild glycolic acid products may also help.

Remedies for acne vary depending on the severity of your breakout. Non-prescription products, useful for the occasional breakout, include benzoyl peroxide or salicylic acid. Antibiotics, Vitamin A derivatives (retinoids) and anti-inflammatory preparations require a prescription. Articles in beauty magazines often suggest treatments, but your dermatologist is the best person to make this decision.

Blackheads are caused when excess oil and dead skin cells clog pores. When these plugs are open to the skin's surface and exposed to air, they turn dark. Don't "squeeze" blackheads. You can rupture the hair follicle causing scarring that permanently enlarges the pore. Try a facial mask or visit an esthetician or dermatologist who knows how to remove blackheads without damaging your skin.

Whiteheads are, essentially, the same thing as a blackhead but they don't get discolored because the excess oil accumulates under the skin.

When you consider how many skin diseases there are, it is amazing that so little, besides the "damage" precipitated by the sun and a blemish outbreak, happens to visible skin. Managing other skin problems goes beyond the scope of this book. Consult your dermatologist for answers to "What is this and what can I do about it?"

Skin Savvy

A facial might seem to be a natural aid in eliminating acne, but they can intensify an existing condition if not performed properly or used when you have a severe breakout.

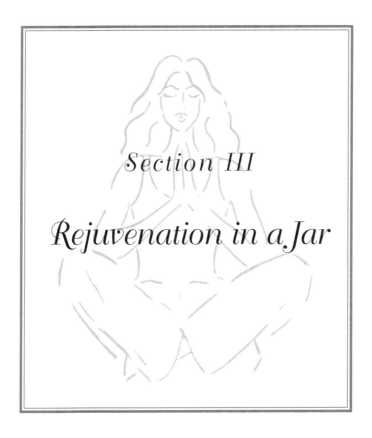

Section III

Rejuvenation in a Jar

"*For every evil under the sun,*
There is a remedy, or there is none,
If there be one, try and find it,
If there be none, never mind it."
                                    Old Nursery Rhyme

12

Cosmetics or Cosmeceuticals ?

It's All on the Label — or Is It?

Despite my degree in pharmacy, I often have difficulty making sense of the words used to market skin care products, much less the ingredients on the bottle or tube used for packaging.

It helps to start by understanding the difference between a cosmetic and a cosmeceutical. According to Webster, a cosmetic is something you use to help correct defects, especially defects of the face. Cosmeceutical is the word (not yet in the dictionary) currently being used to describe a cosmetic product that also treats your skin.

There is more to the story. Anyone can market a cosmetic or a cosmeceutical using words that meet our expressed need to look and feel better. Once a written advertisement makes a claim for a product, things get trickier. There are consumer protection laws that provide guidelines for what a product can and cannot say. These laws separate scientifically proven facts from sales materials, pitches delivered on the internet, magazine ads and articles, information provided at cosmetic counters, TV infomercials featuring high paid actors, doctors or scientists, and solicited or unsolicited testimonials delivered by anyone, anytime, anywhere.

One of the most dramatic ways you can ferret fact from fiction is to look at the bottle or tube used to dispense a product. Despite anything you see or hear, unless a claim is accurate it cannot be put on the vehicle that delivers and dispenses the product to you.

Last, but certainly not least, if the product has an active ingredient, which has been proven to have elements of danger, the regulations for its delivery to the public are even stricter and it will require a prescription.

The U. S. Fair Packaging and Labeling Act (FP&L) regulates how ingredients in skin care products must be listed on a label. The list begins with the ingredient present in the largest concentration (often the necessary "vehicles," like water, necessary to carry another ingredient) until, at the end of the list, you have trace elements and, if present, coloring agents.

There Are Exceptions

If the product also acts as a drug, then the drug is listed prior to all of the cosmetic ingredients regardless of its concentration.

It is not necessary for a product containing a trade secret to list the combination of active ingredients, but the company must submit an application to the FDA in order to list this term and avoid disclosing the ingredients on the label.

Science has revealed what we already knew. Women are blessed with common sense and intuitive wisdom. We often know things work long before it is proven in labs. After years of use to help us feel better, it has now been proven that chicken soup is good for more than the soul. Scientists have also revealed that there are, indeed, potent active ingredients in teas that have been used for centuries to relieve symptoms for a variety of ailments. We want products to work and products that work. We are alive and well and living by the motto, "We can do anything despite the age we are becoming." In skin care, as in life, we want the truth and we don't want to become wrinkled hags waiting for results. We are willing to take responsibility for our decisions including what we will pay for a skin care product that may, or may not, be proven to work and may, or may not, actually work. That includes the option to pay more for your favorite lotion, cream or powder because it smells nice or because you like the consistency or the packaging or the memory of its use by your grandmother. Some people enjoy paying full price for a product in the ambiance of a shop that specializes in expensive skin care products. Others like to buy off the shelf at the discount drug store.

In 1994, some sloppy legislation slipped through the cracks in consumer protection laws and people started selling products as foods, not drugs. This has created havoc in the health and beauty market and precipitated a surge of new skin care products. Some of them have been proven to work in labs but not on humans. These are sold based on testimonials, good marketing strategies, hype and our sincere desire to look and feel better.

As a pharmacist I'm a proponent of the placebo action. If you get the result from a product, use it. Spread the word regarding your success to your sisters. If you spend money for something that doesn't work, don't buy it again. It's called common sense.

Consumers flock to buy products described as "natural." We are willing to pay much more for them even when they cost less to produce than a product that is described as synthetic because it has been created in a laboratory. Bee stings are natural. Bacteria are natural. Poison ivy is natural. That doesn't mean they are good for us. In the skin care field natural usually means there has been little processing of an active ingredient or the product contains no chemical additives. This can be a good thing, but beware. Use of the term natural is not regulated in any way.

Cosmeceuticals: The Four Steps

We didn't call them cosmeceuticals until someone invented the name but it may be an improvement over the bland description: skin care products. The smorgasbord of products fall into a wide range of categories but most skin care specialists recommend you do four things to care for your skin:

1. Cleanse the skin:

Since most skin problems come from pores that get clogged, keeping your face clean may be the most important prevention strategy you can muster. The goal is to remove the bad stuff and leave what your skin needs to protect you from the elements.

Most experts recommend you keep cleansing to a

minimum. In addition to the morning cleansing that helps you start your day and the evening cleansing that assures you remove accumulated dirt and makeup, you probably only need to freshen your skin with a product like the new packaged mild soap saturated face wipes. If you exercise, you will want to add an additional cleansing to remove perspiration, pollutants and excess oil your effort may precipitate.

2.   Exfoliate the skin:

Exfoliates go beyond our body's natural ability to shed skin or removal of dead skin cells that occurs when your clothes rub against your skin or you towel off after a shower. They make skin look smoother by getting rid of the top layer of dead skin cells and exposing the newer ones underneath.

The range of products used for exfoliating skin go from something as simple as my favorite, OLAY DAILY FACIALS, which provide just the "right" amount of exfoliation, to the use of procedures and harsh products that require the skilled eye, hand and administration by a physician. As one dermatologist told me, "Scrubbing is for counters and floors, not skin." Be careful when using these products—especially if you have acne.

3.   Moisturize the skin:

Most people believe that moisturizers replace moisture. They don't. They create a barrier between your skin and the air. Moisturizers are designed to trap the skin's water. This prevents the skin's natural moisture from evaporating. It gives the skin a smoother appearance. Moisturizers transform dry or itchy skin but can clog the pores of oily skin.

Most people have combination skin. That means you apply moisturizer in spots rather than over your entire face. You may also want to use a lotion on one place and cream on another. The product you use may vary depending on where you are on a given day. Those of us who travel for work may use one product in the hot climate of sun belt states and a different in the wetter climate of the Pacific Northwest and a third in the drier, colder winters of the Midwest.

4.   Protect from further damage:

There continues to be an Email making the rounds on the internet that claims to be the advice of a famous writer delivered at a graduation ceremony. In fact, it was written by a newspaper reporter for publication in a small paper. The first and last line of advice is: "Wear sunscreen." You read all you need to know about sun damage in chapter nine. Read it again, and again, and again, and be sure to follow the advice there. Wear sunscreen.

Beyond these four steps you are dealing with products that solve skin problems, refresh the appearance of the skin and rejuvenate your face. They tune, tone and tighten skin. There are so many that for more information about them you need to go directly to your favorite skin care specialist. If you can't get the answers you need without being pressed into a purchase, try somewhere else. Library resources tend to be behind the times but your favorite book store will have so many options there is sure to be a couple that will turn you on and become one of your wisest non-breathing friends.

Cosmetics

The size and number of cosmetic (make-up) counters seem to be expanding in direct relationship to the number of baby boomers moving past age fifty. They turn up in hair salons, department and drug stores, spas, malls and, WOW, there are cosmetic counters where you can test new colors in airports while you wait for a plane. (This is a very good marketing strategy.) For an introduction to the cosmetic know-how, hang on until Chapter 19.

Cleansers   This is no longer "just" about soap. Yes,
             Ivory is still 99.44-100% pure and there
             are super-fatted, transparent and soapless
             soaps (isn't that an oxymoron?). Now you
             also get to choose between a foaming
             cleanser, gel cleanser, lotion cleanser
             (water-soluble or oil free), cleansing milks
             and more, delivered in saturated cloths,
             tubes and breakable and unbreakable jars.

Exfoliates   To remove the top layer of dead skin cells
             you will be asked if you want a saturated
             cloth, wash cloth, silk mitt, synthetic
             loofah, grainy mask, buffing cream or an
             antioxidant, fruit acid or concentrated
             vitamin derivative (just to name a few).

Moisturizers Is it animal, vegetable or mineral? When
             you purchase a moisturizer you will be
             able to choose between oil-free lotions and
             gels made from molecules that can't
             penetrate skin, glycerin based products,
             and the products that contain a wide
             range of animal, vegetable or mineral oils.

Protection   Use SPF, protective clothing, sunglasses
             and ignore anyone who says "a little sun
             won't hurt you." See chapter nine.

13

What Is In Those Jars?

Remember, in chapter nine, where I revealed the stunning number of sun protection products? That list pales when it comes to the number of active and inactive ingredients in skin care products.

When you are cleaning, exfoliating, moisturizing and protecting those ingredients fall into classes of products with names that describe their use. For example, there are:

1. Binding Agents: Substances that hold products together and prevent separation of the water and lipid components.

2. Emollients: Substances that smooth and soften the skin. There are literally several hundred emollients, each providing its own individual texture to the skin.

3. Emulsion: A blend of oil and water into a single smooth product.

4. Humectants: Substances that can attract water, usually out of the air. By definition, all humectants are also moisturizers.

5. Lubricants: Substances that make skin feel smoother to the touch and reduce friction.
6. Preservatives: Substances that kill detrimental bacteria, yeast and/or molds, thus preventing spoilage. (Preservatives are *not* a bad thing.)
7. Solvents: Substances, such as alcohol or water, which dissolve other ingredients.
8. Surfactants: Substances that enable a topical product to easily spread and glide across skin.
9. Vehicle: The base that carries the active ingredients.

Skin care (cosmeceutical) companies put ingredients that, in addition to cleansing, exfoliating, moisturizing and protecting, perform all those actions into their products.

It is no wonder we look to books, doctors, skin care specialists and our girlfriends hoping to find a way to ferret through the conflicting information about which product is good for skin health and beauty.

I have a guideline that never fails me. When confused, go back to basics. For the purpose of skin care, start by considering the anatomy of skin and how it works. This will narrow your options.

Skin is a protective organ. Not much can penetrate its outer layers. If you remember that, it makes it easier to decide for yourself whether what you read or hear does, or doesn't, make sense.

Despite the limits of penetration to any but the very top layers there are many "active" and "inactive" ingredients in the skin care products that sit on the counters and line the shelves and fill the bins of a variety of stores, home beauty parties and spas. The thought of listing even a few examples is mind boggling. Moreover, I don't want someone putting a contract out on my life or writing Emails accusing me of bias, ignoring their product or barraging me because they disagree with my opinion. So, let's switch gears and become generalists.

Skin care products fall into three catagories. The first group contains hundreds of products, which are easily accessible and mostly harmless to skin. They range from animal products (lanolin from sheep, for example); plant products, now called botanicals (aloe vera, for example); and mineral products (glycerin and vaseline, for example) that formed the nucleus of products sold back "in the olden days" to newer products with fancy names like mucopolysaccharides, as well as enzymes and synthetic products. Some work and some don't.

Hydroquinone, an ingredient that is in skin-bleaching creams, is an example of a product that does work. If used on a regular basis for a long time, it can lighten age spots. These products are marketed as bleaching creams even though they don't typically bleach the skin. Instead, they inhibit melanin production on the areas where the cream is applied. If you use these products, you must keep treated areas out of the sun or you will defy the purpose of the cream. Some products are also packaged with fruit acids (see below).

On the other hand there are many products that don't have anything but testimonials from users to back them up. These include products with collagen and elastin ingredients that, despite claims, *never* penetrate the skin, vitamins that may or may not exist, topical hormones that are not in sufficient concentration to do anything for skin and other ingredients with creamy or scientific sounding names. Whether they are helpful, harmful or overrated seems to be an individual experience.

The second category includes the exciting antioxidants, once glorified only for their disease preventing properties when captured by your body from food. It turns out they are also skin savers. The next chapter is devoted to these vitamins, minerals and other plant substances which are appropriately generating so much media attention.

The third category includes the hottest (figuratively and literally) skin care products on the market, the fruit acids. You probably know them as AHAs and BHAs. These products come in various concentrations that can be purchased over-the-counter and prescribed, in stronger strengths, by your physician. They are the basis for peels done by dermatologists. Chapter 15 is devoted to these newest wrinkle-reducers.

Regardless of the product, and where you ultimately purchase it, choosing the one that is right for you is an individual decision.

An Unabashed Testimonial

Companies like OLAY are doing an exemplary job of creating high quality products at affordable prices. This is a case where there is something for everybody. I like OLAY because they are so generous with their samples. You only have to pop onto their internet site: http://www.olay.com and click on the free sample icon, fill out your mailing address and the postman will deliver your own self testing trial package. All of their products have SPF protection, they are packaged beautifully, feel good and, quite honestly, are, I believe, responsible for me reaching my late fifties with few wrinkles despite too much sun exposure.

When you meet a person who is attempting to sell you a skin care product be aware they are either:
- ✓ a salesperson who knows nothing about the product
- ✓ a salesperson with minimum training from beauty companies whose products are sold in the venue

✓   a person who is trained in and sells only one product line (usually employees at a department store who are often paid on commission)

✓   a person well trained in many products and handles many lines (usually at a spa or salon)

✓   a person who knows and likes a product and creates an agreement with the manufacturer to "private label" it with an individual's name

✓   a person trained to sell product from home

✓   the rare person who has created his or her own product

These are good people who are sincerely enthusiastic about the products they sell. Because some of them don't know about skin anatomy and biochemistry, they rely on employers, trainers or what they read or hear from others. While researching this book I discovered there are many popular skin care and skin nutrition books written by "experts" with degrees from prestigious universities. Many of these books were enthusiastically recommended to me by women who want to know more about looking and feeling good and want to believe that what they read is true. I, in turn, read with the jaundiced eye of a pharmacist and scientist and discovered that, as usual, when someone is off the deep end with a *new* theory that flies in the face of research it may sound logical but "it ain't necessarily so." As you read earlier, I believe new theories are good, but I am also a product of my experience and I've watched more skin care (and nutrition, diet and weight management) products and programs hit the market, make money for a while, disappear and leave the unwary buyer wondering, "What happened?"

Just remember the adage, "Buyers, beware." Then, talk to your girlfriends. Ask for samples. Invest in a full sized bottle—it is worth it if only for the adventure of discovering if you and the product are a perfect match. Engage that savvy intuition that makes being a woman so exciting. Buy for convenience, ambiance, service or whatever turns you on. Looking and feeling beautiful is about having fun. There is nothing more fun than hitting a cosmetic counter with a few of my girlfriends to poke through and test products or sit in that swiveled, high chair for a complimentary makeover the afternoon before a fancy party. It is fulfillment of the fantasy we shared the first time we secretly picked up a tube of our mother's lipstick. It is about being a girl.

14

The Antioxidants

A Free Radical Is Not from Berkeley

When I was in Pharmacy school, I learned that I could soften rough, dry patches of skin by breaking open a capsule of vitamin E and rubbing it on the affected area. Since then, the power of vitamin E (and other nutrients) to protect our skin (and body) has become so important that it is the leading ingredient in many skin creams.

Vitamin E is one of the many nutrients that fall into a category called antioxidants. Our body's cells require oxygen for their work. In the normal course of that work it releases a cell damaging, unstable oxygen molecule called a free radical. When we are young, our body quickly mobilizes vitamins, minerals, enzymes and other compounds to stabilize free radicals. This ability to control damage decreases because an aging body has a declining ability to repair itself. Additionally, we are exposed to the accumulative effects of pollution, fried foods, tobacco smoke and other environmental challenges that accelerate the production of these free radicals. If we aren't eating a healthy, antioxidant-rich diet, our body doesn't have access to the stabilizing antioxidants so free radicals attack a healthy cell to, in effect, steal what it needs. This creates a domino effect that can result in more damaged cells than healthy ones. An environment of damaged cells supports the development of many of the diseases of aging. Even if you could protect yourself from further production of free radicals, or if your body could repair 99% of all damage, the backlog of old debris would continue to do its dirty work.

Research reveals that the most potent antioxidants are Vitamin E, Vitamin C, the carotenoids (precursors of Vitamin A), selenium and zinc. Because these nutrients are in fruits, vegetables, nuts and seeds you are hearing more about the need to eat more complex carbohydrates—the primary category of foods that contain antioxidants. There are also antioxidants in teas that are being shown to be useful in protecting the skin from sun damage as well as the inflammation and swelling that free radical damage generates.

You can take these antioxidants as a supplement, but because nutrients don't work in a vacuum, and because they tend to synergize one another, it is best when you get these powerhouses of repair in a balanced and varied diet. (See Chapter 24.)

Nutrition Savvy

Even when your diet is well balanced, the stresses of daily life can deplete your body of the vitamins and minerals essential to healthy skin. A multivitamin is insurance to support good nutrition that should start with food.

Antioxidants and Skin

Although antioxidants do great work inside the body, it appears they never reach the surface of the skin. Learning this, savvy cosmeceutical companies began adding them to skin care creams believing they could prevent further damage from the outside in. Research is showing it works. Better yet, it appears that putting antioxidants on top of your skin may stimulate the production of collagen in deeper layers. Combining these potent scavengers and healers with sun protection *may* be the greatest present you can give your skin. Add moisturizing properties and you have a best case scenario for an over-the-counter product to keep you from deteriorating from the outside in.

At this time, vitamin C and beta carotene applied before you go out in the sun, and vitamin E (remember that capsule I broke apart?) used within eight hours after you are in the sun, are shown to turn back the damage caused by ultraviolet rays that generate skin damaging free radicals.

Retinol, a derivative of fat soluble Vitamin A, can reduce the appearance of fine lines and wrinkles but it is only one-tenth as effective as its prescription cousin, tretinoin (sold as Avita™, Renova®, Retin-A®, Retin-A® Micro™).

It turns out that tea is more than a soothing drink. Tea is filled with many antioxidant plant components that have made it useful for more than 3000 years for its health benefits. Although most of these are of use internally (the caffeine as a stimulant or theophylline that helps open breathing passages, for example) tea also has been shown to be useful to protect the skin from ultra violet radiation. It is soothing to skin (remember those wet, cool tea bags on closed eyelids to remove puffiness) as an anti-inflammatory—a key characteristic of antioxidants on skin.

The interest in antioxidants is so overwhelming it would take a whole book to discuss their many sources and uses. *Age Proof Your Body* by dietitian, Elizabeth Somer, is the place to start. You can't go wrong with antioxidants (preferably from food) to help keep the inside of your body disease free. I'd bet money the same will be true for external use of these free radical scavengers.

Alpha Lipoic Acids

There is currently a lot of interest in a metabolite scientists call a coenzyme as a possible defensive agent for use against free radicals. Alpha lipoic acid may recycle and extend the lifespan of antioxidants in the body—especially when combined with Vitamin C. Because Vitamin C is useful as an external skin antioxidant there is a growing body of evidence that a low-in-strength alpha lipoic acid may be useful as a treatment for wrinkles. Most of the attention has been generated by the doctor who has conducted studies of alpha lipoic acid. The studies showed that it has skin renewal properties, which after 6-8 weeks of use diminish scarring caused by acne. The product is marketed by a book, authored by the doctor, packaged and sold (at $85 for 2 oz.!) by a company he owns. In other words, use your own discretion and/or stay tuned.

Vitamin C Serums, Esters and Patches

Despite the selling of billions of dollars of Vitamin C solutions, serums and patches in recent years, I was unable to find any credible, independent, published evidence that these potent products are as miraculous as the companies who sell them purport them to be. Once again, try and, if you like it, buy it.

Although they are not antioxidants the B vitamins can enhance the performance of antioxidants in skin care products and cosmetics. They work by standing alongside the pathways that keep these antioxidants working to prevent free radical damage. In an industrial plant they would be called expediters. In skin care they are called co-factors. Vitamin B3 (niacinamide) and Vitamin B5 (panthenol) are two important vitamins that facilitate this action, especially when combined with Vitamin E.

I remember when a healthy diet and a pair of sturdy walking shoes was the best equipment I could muster to defy age. Now, with added sun and skin protection offered by SPF and antioxidants in creams and makeup, I have many powerful weapons to help me look as good as I feel. Once again, girls have all the fun.

15

The Fruit Acids

Her Story

When, after a serious discussion about drugs, my friend's daughter asked, "Mom, since you went to college in the sixties, did you ever use acid?" she was stunned to hear her mother say, "I use it now."

She quickly added, "I'm kidding. I'm talking about the fruit acids I put on my face for skin care."

Although knowledge of the beauty benefits of fruit acids date back centuries (think Cleopatra's milk baths) it was the nineties before they hit the market as a wonder skin remedy. They are used in over-the-counter cleansers, lotions, and other products. Higher concentrations of these acids are applied in salons or doctor's offices where they are called mini-peels or chemical peels.

Now smart women are snapping these products up like crazy. They improve the skin by peeling away (exfoliating) the uppermost layers of the skin. Exfoliation, you will remember, speeds skin rejuvenation by revealing smoother, younger-looking (and more sensitive) skin.

Fruit Acid Primer

Fruit acids fall into two categories.

Alpha Hydroxy Acids (AHAs)

The first category, alpha hydroxy acids (AHAs), got the initial round of attention. There are sixteen that come from a variety of sources including the most common:

✓ sugar cane (glycolic acid) (the most popular and best penetration)
✓ fruit (citric acid)
✓ apples and pears (malic acid)
✓ milk (lactic acid)
✓ grapes (tartaric acid)
✓ synthetic products created in a laboratory

Alpha hydroxy acids give the skin a healthy glow by accelerating skin turnover (exfoliation), which exposes healthier skin cells and, possibly, stimulates the production of collagen and elastin. They come in a dizzying array of percentages including some products that don't have enough fruit acid to do anything at all and others that may have too much for *your* skin.

Finding the right AHA product can be a challenge because there are five factors that determine how "potent" it will be on an individual's skin:

1. where the product is used (skin location);
2. which acid is used – glycolic and lactic acid are the two most popular acids used;

(Glycolic acid is more potent because it penetrates skin faster. If you use it and your skin gets irritated, switching to less irritating lactic acid may bring relief.)

3. the concentration, or percentage, of acid used. Obviously, higher is stronger;

4. whether the person using the product is exposed to sun after its use;

5. the pH* (or acidity) of the vehicle or base in which the AHA is distributed.

pH is a measure of the acidity of the skin. A value of 7 is a measure of neutrality. If something has a pH of 7 or less it is described as acidic. If something has a pH of 7 or more, it is described as alkaline.

A highly concentrated AHA in an acidic base or vehicle (low pH) will be stronger than a product with a lower concentration in an alkaline base (high pH). Each will produce a different result depending on whether it is applied to the (for example) more sensitive skin of the face or the (for example) slightly less sensitive skin of the back of the hands.

There is also controversy about whether AHAs are cosmetics or drugs. According to a sixty year old Federal Food, Drug and Cosmetic Act, cosmetics are about products that can be rubbed, poured, sprinkled or sprayed on to skin in order to cleanse, beautify, promote attractiveness or alter appearance. They do not require pre-market review or approval before they can be sold to the public. On the other hand, if a product treats or prevents disease or affects the structure or function of the body, it must be tested and reviewed for safety before public use.

For the time being, the cosmetic industry's self-regulatory body is meeting these standards:

✓ AHA products sold to consumers have an AHA concentration of 10 percent or less (and a pH of 3.5 or higher).
✓ AHA products used by trained and certified cosmetologists (estheticians) may run between 10 and 30 percent. (They tend to be wise and use higher percentages and sell lower percentages.)
✓ AHA products used by doctors can range from 50 to 70 percent. They are called "peels."

If you use an AHA product:
- **buy a product with a concentration of 10 percent or less and a pH of 3.5 or more**
- **do a sensitivity test on a patch of skin before you use any AHA product for the first time (including if you change brands or product concentration)**
- **STOP using a product if it causes stinging, redness, itching, burning, pain, bleeding or a change in your sensitivity to the sun (products should never hurt you)**
- **and have an adverse reaction, see a dermatologist immediately**

Skin Savvy

The best way to try an AHA for the first time is in the form of a lightweight moisturizer with a concentration of less than 5 percent and pH of 5 or more. If your skin tolerates it well, you can move up in strength in a step by step fashion.

Beta Hydroxy Acids (BHAs)

The second category of fruit acids is called beta hydroxy acids (BHAs). (These are sometimes called alpha-beta hydroxy acids.)

There are four beta hydroxy acids. The most common in skin care products is salicylic acid. However, it is not a BHA at all. It is a good example of how marketing and media can change science into perceived reality by saying something so often it becomes culturally accepted. This derivative of aspirin (acetyl salicylic acid) has been used to treat acne, dandruff, psoriasis and corns on the feet for years. Now salicylic acid is gaining in popularity in the skin care field because it appears to be as effective as AHAs but less irritating to the skin. This is probably because, unlike the fruit acids, it is soluble in oil so it can get down to the skin follicle. Some professionals believe that in addition to its role as an exfoliant, salicylic acid shares aspirin's ability to decrease inflammation and the swelling that often goes with it.

To be effective as an exfoliant, a BHA must have a concentration of one to two percent. Putting it in an alkaline vehicle with a pH of 4 or 5 neutralizes it. It is no longer effective. On the other hand, a low pH (more acidic) makes it too irritating. A pH of about 3 appears to be ideal.

Over-the-counter fruit acid products can lessen the degree of apparent damage to skin by the sun and other factors. Everyone I know who uses them (including me) swears by them. However, only prescription products and treatments by a dermatologist can lessen the degree of damage and turn back the hands of time.

The exfoliation properties of fruit acids can reduce the ability of the skin to retain moisture. The redness, dryness and irritation they can produce make moisturizing an essential part of skin beauty and skin health.

Skin Savvy

If you have non-Caucasian skin, don't use AHA products until you've tested them on a hidden section of your skin for several days to be sure they don't generate changes in your skin's pigment.

Fruit Acids as Skin Peels

If you want the more dramatic results fruit acids can offer, you need to consult a dermatologist who will examine your skin and, based on experience, recommend the appropriate peel for you. See page 114 for an overview of the options.

16

The Doctor Is In

When the science of creating or enhancing beauty needs a helping hand it turns to a well trained professional who can help correct real and imagined defects in a person's face and skin. The medical community stands ready to respond to the demand to make perception and reality, regarding our self-image, meet.

A dermatologist is a doctor who is an expert in the treatment of disorders of the skin. A plastic surgeon specializes in reducing scarring or disfigurement that may occur as a result of accidents, birth defects or treatment for diseases (such as melanoma).

Now these two specialties are, in many cases, overlapping. Dermatologists have aggressively responded to the demand for the treatment of "aging" (we know it is damaged) skin. Plastic surgeons are now sub-specialized into cosmetic or aesthetic surgeons whose entire practice is dedicated to attempting to turn back time and re-sculpting the face and body.

If your skin doesn't respond to an over-the-counter routine, there are prescription products that can offer more aggressive therapy. Additionally, there are treatments that can puff depressions, smooth lines, eliminate scars and re-sculpt and augment facial skin, muscle and bone.

Your Pharmacist Is In

You can spend a lot of money on cosmetic products and facial treatments to slow damage from photoaging but only one prescription product has been approved for wrinkle reduction. Retin A (generic name tretinoin) is a naturally occurring form of Vitamin A, which was originally approved for acne treatment. Dermatologists using the product noticed their patients experienced a reduction in the fine wrinkles, age spots and skin roughness caused by skin exposure. Now this retinoic acid is available as Renova® in a cream and liquid approved for these uses. It sloughs off dead skin, regenerates collagen and allows cells in the top layer of skin, which are always being replaced, to mature more normally than untreated sun-damaged cells.

There have been no studies in the use of tretinoin in women over age fifty. It doesn't reverse the aging process and doesn't repair sun-damaged skin. If tretinoin is prescribed for you, you must continue to use it if you want the results to last. Since it sensitizes the skin to the sun, tanning is forbidden and daily use of a SPF 30 sunscreen is necessary. In other words, when added to a comprehensive, formerly unsuccessful, skin care and sun avoidance program it often provides the added jump start needed to diminish fine lines and wrinkles.

Deep Peels

Chemical peels create a controlled inflammation in the skin's outer layers prompting the skin to shed. When it does, fresh, smooth skin is exposed and superficial wrinkles and some pigmentation irregularities disappear.

Peels come in various concentrations, which describe how deeply the chemicals invade the skin. Light peels keep skin clear and glowing. Deep peels, which have a rejuvenating effect on skin's collagen, leave skin more supple and elastic, but also carry more risk and recovery time. Your skin may flake or peel a few days after the peel, but flaking or peeling usually subsides quickly. Very deep peels generate a scab that will last for about ten days and skin that is pink for about three months. WARNING: The downside of a deep peel is that if your physician is not highly skilled you may be left with small scars, and your skin will be permanently lighter and more susceptible to sunburn. Chemical peels can cause blotchy skin in people with darker skin.

Who Can	Penetrate the Layers	Of Skin
You	Rubbing against clothing	Epidermis
You	Towelling off	Epidermis
You	Scrubs at home	Epidermis
You	Facial masks at home	Epidermis
Esthetician	Glycolic peel	Epidermis
Dermatologist	TCA peel	Dermis
Dermatologist	Peenol peel	Dermis
Dermatologist	Dermabrasion	Dermis
Dermatologist	Laser peel	Dermis

How Peels Work

Kind of Peel:	*Used For:*	*Recovery Time:*
Light peel uses a 30-70 percent concentration of one of the AHA's (usually glycolic acid)	Scaly, blotchy skin, fine lines and, in younger skin, prevents and clears up blemishes; restores skin's "glow"	Up to 2 weeks for redness to subside (depends on strength of acid)
Medium peel uses a 10-30 percent concentration of trichloroacetic acid	Skin that has been moderately to severely damaged by the sun (deeper wrinkles) or to even out marked pigmentation; sometimes used on the hands; good for "spot" peels of specific areas	Make up usually ok after 3-7 days; ten days to look presentable; normal skin tone in several weeks
Deep peel uses phenol (requires expert medical care and usually done in an operating room environment); Buffered peels are slightly milder; Deep peel not used much anymore because lasers work as well and have fewer health risks	Deep wrinkles and severely sun-damaged skin; repairs severe pigmentation problems; removes and prevents pre-cancerous and cancerous lesions	48 hours bed rest recommended after treatment; post-op pain may require prescription painkillers; sun exposure is strictly forbidden after this treatment

How Often	Comments
Can be repeated every 3-4 weeks; Usually about four treatments; Most physicians build to higher concentrations of acids over a series of visits	Removes outer layers of the epidermis and encourages cell regeneration; takes about 15 minutes; a tingling sensation during the peel; face becomes slightly pink; some tenderness just after the peel followed by visible flaking for 3-4 days
Six months minimum between treatments	Reaches top of the dermis; takes about 30 minutes; mildly painful; some patients ask for sedation depending on depth of the peel; superficial layers of the skin redden and swell and sometimes ooze; skin becomes crusty then peels; aftercare instructions must be carefully followed to prevent scarring
One treatment	Reaches the middle of the dermis; takes about 30 minutes; sedation is used; skin is red, swollen and oozy for 8-10 days until scabs form; scabs slough off in 2-3 weeks; skin is normal in 3-6 months; not suitable for dark skin

Collagen Injections

Collagen is the natural protein that provides the supportive webbing in the dermis of the skin. Collagen injections use a collagen derived from cow skin to rejuvenate the skin by plumping up individual wrinkles and depressed scars and for wrinkles around the eyes and mouth. They are currently popular in the entertainment industry to give women an appearance of fuller lips. The body absorbs the injected collagen so the benefits are temporary. To sustain the desired effects, re-injection is required every 6 to 12 months.

Botox Injections

Botulism is a deadly toxin found in uncooked foods. It paralyzes muscles. A purified form of the toxin was originally used, medically, to stop facial tics by injecting the toxin into the muscles causing the tics. Now it is being used to paralyze muscles that cause wrinkling or furrowing of the skin of the forehead and around the eyes. If you can't move the muscles, the injected site stays smooth. The effects of a botox injection wear off after about four months but the "use it or lose it" principle of muscle work kicks in and there is often a reduction in the ability to contract the muscle itself. If the muscles you choose to paralyze with this injection have been a critical part of your facial expression be sure you realize that will no longer be the case.

Fat Transplants

Most people don't think of body fat as anything that is alive. We believe it just sits under our skin and jiggles. Fat is alive. A doctor can make a small incision in your buttocks or thigh, remove fat, treat it and put it somewhere else. If it links to underlying blood supply it will stay in the injected place permanently. If it doesn't link, it will be absorbed by the body over a six month period.

Fat transplants are used to "plump" depressions anywhere on your face and body. The doctor will tightly wrap the site from which the fat is removed to prevent a depression there. Smile lines, the backs of hands and pitted scars are common injection sites. This is a relatively painless but somewhat expensive procedure. Intriguing to say the least.

(Micro) Dermabrasion

In dermabrasion fine wrinkles, age spots and scars can be "sanded down" with a small, rotating wheel. Scabbing and swelling generally last a couple of weeks. Complete healing takes longer. The downside is that there is often a different character of skin where the dermabrasion takes place causing an uneven tone in the color of the skin.

Laser Resurfacing

This appears to be the most effective exfoliation method for eliminating wrinkles. To understand lasers you need a background in science. Basically a laser highly energizes atoms of light. When a doctor directs these precisely delivered bursts of light at your skin it vaporizes wrinkles and shrinks the underlying skin (collagen) fibers. Lasers can target large areas of skin, such as the entire face, or select problems, such as spider veins, acne scars or spot resurfacing to remedy wrinkles around the mouth or eyes.

There are two kind of lasers. The carbon dioxide laser is more powerful and is used for deep wrinkles and skin imperfections. A newer laser called a YAG or Erbium laser is gentler and is used to smooth surfaces. Some surgeons use both and combine computer directed lasers with freehand use of the tool.

Laser resurfacing can be shallow and done in a doctor's office, or deep, which requires a surgical environment. Post procedure discomfort, appearance and recovery are based on the depth of the treatment. It is not something you can do on your lunch hour but it takes less recovery time than cosmetic surgery.

With so many options for the treatment of damaged skin, dermatologists, cosmetic surgeons and patients have a wide variety of medical, surgical, prescription drug and cosmetic treatments available to create the desired results. When these procedures aren't enough, you can always turn to a cosmetic surgeon.

17

Cosmetic Surgery: When Nothing Else Works

"Act your age."

"Grow old gracefully."

It's easy to say when we are young. It's another thing when, later in life, you discover that the person in the mirror isn't someone you know. If this is the case, in time, something may trigger your interest in "plastic" surgery.

Plastic surgery was "born" after severe damage to the faces, skin and limbs of WWI soldiers inspired surgeons to create reconstructive techniques that often used devices made from plastic. When optional surgeries, such as "a little tuck," "nose jobs" and breast augmentation became popular plastic surgery became cosmetic surgery. Now it is also called aesthetic cosmetic surgery. The three terms are used inter-changeably.

Cosmetic surgical and non-surgical procedures number close to five million a year. New polls show that the majority of Americans now approve of cosmetic surgery. Eighty-two percent of women now say that, if they had cosmetic surgery in the future, they would not be embarrassed if people outside their immediate family/close friends knew about it. This is a dramatic cultural shift from fifty years ago when these "procedures" were a secret and deemed suitable *only* for rich, self-indulgent women who had nothing better to do with their time. Women returned from lengthy vacations with new haircuts, glasses and a refreshed look they attributed to rest. Rhinoplasty (a "nose job") was defended with the excuse that it helped a woman to breathe more easily. We may not have liked the humor of Phyllis Diller but we couldn't wait to see what her face looked like.

Traditional cosmetic surgery can correct drooping upper eyelids, remove bags and circles beneath your eyes, improve sagging facial skin, lift a furrowed forehead and make wrinkles disappear. A surgeon can implant cheeks and chins and sculpt a nose. Breasts can be augmented or diminished and fat can be removed by excision or suction. The use of cosmetic surgery by younger and younger clients is coming out of the closet and accepted as an alternative to life inside skin that stretches physically as we stretch emotionally.

Here's an overview of what is available.

The Facelift Experience
(This includes only the most common procedures.)

Upper Blepharoplasty — Upper Eyelid Lift

Repairs a drooping eyelid. Removes fat pouches, extra skin and wrinkles around the upper eye. Scars are positioned in the upper eyelid groove just above the crease.Upper and lower blepharoplasty is the number-one facial procedure in cosmetic surgery.

Lower Blepharoplasty — Lower Eyelid Lift
Removes puffiness, fat pouches, extra skin and wrinkles under the eye. You can't diet away under eye fat. Scars are under the lower eyelashes.

Forehead Lift — Brow Lift
Moves eyebrows to brow bone, smoothes furrows in the forehead and improves the look of upper eyelids. More frequently, this is done with an endoscope to minimize cutting. It is an adjunct to eye surgery.

SMAS (superficial musculo-aponeurotic system) Lift — Face Lift
Detaches and repositions soft tissues and muscles of the face and neck. Excess skin is excised. Requires an incision that varies depending on doctor and technique. There is no "one size fits all" SMAS It varies from surgeon to surgeon and face to face.

Rhinoplasty — Nose Sculpture
Alters the appearance of the nose. Regarded as one of the most difficult by surgeons because of the complex structure of the nose.

Cheek Lift — Cheek Lift
A facelift that elevates the mid-face but not the chin and throat.

Cheek Augmentation — Cheek Implant
Used in bone deficient sites. Cheeks can be "lifted" on patients whose skin has simply dropped. With or without the implant, the procedure is done from inside the mouth.

Mentoplasty — Chin Implant or Chin Augmentation
Permanently reshapes a receding chin. Incision can be under the skin or through the mouth. Often combined with rhinoplasty to improve the profile of the face.

Other common procedures (as long as we're on the subject) include:

Breast Augmentation — Breast Implant
Increases breast size. Demand for this decreased when post-surgical illnesses developed. There are a variety of implants available.

Breast Reduction — Breast Reduction
Reduces pendulous breasts. Nipple is detached then replaced at proper location. Scarring occurs.

Liposuction — Liposuction
Removal of fat to re-contour an area of the body. Your insurance company will not pay for this popular surgery. It is best utilized to remove stubborn fat pads on fit people. It is *not* an alternative to exercise and sensible eating. If you gain weight, it will settle someplace else.

Abdominoplasty — Tummy Tuck
Removes excess skin and fat and tightens abdominal muscles. Usually is combined with liposuction.

Her Story

In 1999, I left an important professional relationship that had endured for years despite a series of roller coaster emotional swings. When I left, I not only lost the professional collaboration but the camaraderie and lengthy friendships that went with it.

After the initial jubilation of taking care of myself, I felt sad. I believe attitude is everything, but I couldn't shake this feeling. I turned to a mental health professional who listened to me complain about my inability to tap into the resiliency skills I'd forged in recent years.

She said, "Ronda, you are experiencing grief. Perhaps, at the time, you didn't appropriately grieve many of the (other) major losses you've described. Maybe it is this last loss that's thrown you over the edge. We could spend months delving into why you avoided this healing process or you can dive in and do some grief recovery work."

I took the plunge. It was painful, but combined with coping strategies I'd learned earlier in life, I came out the other side filled with hope and verve and excitement about the possibilities for the remainder of my life. I was newly immersed in work that stirred passions and gratified me. In short, I had everything going for me. But, when I looked in the mirror, reviewed a video of a TV appearance or looked at a photo, the Ronda I saw looked extraordinarily sad and tired despite a now recovered emotional state. I had a look of despair. My jowls were deeper than ever. Contraction of my under the chin muscles only made the jowls jiggle. It was funny. It was not funny.

Synchronicity prevailed. At just the right moment a remarkable friend and entertainer invited me to her weekly performance. "I want you to see my facelift," she added.

When I saw my friend I was stunned to realize that her jowls were gone. She looked the same but remarkably rested, younger and vibrant.

"I've been thinking about 'doing that,'" I shared.

"You must call my surgeon. He's a genius."

In reality I "interviewed" three potential surgeons. I "chose" the same one as my friend, and after considerable preparation agreed to a facelift and, because I wanted to remove the sad and tired appearance on my face, upper and lower eyelid surgery. I had complete confidence it would be a life-changing experience. I wasn't disappointed.

Cosmetic surgery isn't for everyone. There are probably those who would chastise me and ask why I couldn't find these traits within me without going "under the knife." I wish I could say I understood. I only know that post-surgery I returned to physical, mental, social, emotional and spiritual health with some indescribable sense of self that my psychologically based skills could not achieve. If it took a surgeon's steady hand to remove the sorrow etched on my face by the death of beloved parents, the end of a lengthy marriage, loss of a valuable professional relationship, and to physically erase the sleeplessness acquired during the years I nursed a chronically ill child, the jump start it gave me into my new way of being in the world was well worth it.

A Common Question, or Two

The most common questions I receive when I talk about the facelift experience described above are, "Did it hurt?" and "How much did it cost?"

The answer is to the first is, "No." I chose an after-care center for my initial recovery. When I emerged from my anesthesia I was certain God was punishing me for my unwillingness to be happy with that tired, sad and jowled face I'd been seeing in the mirror. Internally, I pleaded for forgiveness. Externally, I asked for a pain pill. I took it, went back to sleep and, subsequently, needed only Tylenol for relief from discomfort that is caused by the shift in tissues and the swelling it precipitates. (You will never look uglier.)

As for cost, I discovered that though you will read surveys that estimate costs, they vary based on choice of doctor, where you live and what procedures you choose. It is rarely covered by health insurance.

Recovery

When my bandages were removed two days post-op (it *is* an operation), I cried when a friend who faithfully recorded everything, day-by-day, with his digital camera showed me a front and side view of my face. My jowls were gone.

I was an exemplary patient and my recovery went without a hitch, although it took longer than I hoped (and the exact time my surgeon warned me it would take). It was several weeks before I felt comfortable going out in public despite a lesson in camouflage makeup that was part of a post-surgery follow-up visit to my competent doc. It took longer for me to get back to an active lifestyle than I planned because each time I exercised, my face responded as it always had. It temporarily swelled. Swelling is the enemy for recovery from a face lift. So, I opted for occasional long walks with no increase in intensity. My fitness level sunk to a lifetime low.

I made one serious error. Before surgery, in an effort to prepare myself for a quick recovery, I exercised and ate nothing but "healthy" food and lost about eight pounds of fat. Subsequent to surgery, when I was not hungry, I lost five more pounds. I was at the low weight I never expected to see on the scale again. Maintaining a consistent, pre-surgery weight is, I discovered later, the goal if you want the results of your surgery to be maintained. Eighteen months after surgery I teach an exercise class every day and eat wisely most of the time but, thanks to that six month period of low activity and resumption of "normal" eating habits, I've gained weight, then resettled into what I believe is "normal" for me. If, as I've been told, that one time yo-yo will reduce the effects of the surgery, timewise, it is okay with me—today. I'm sixty-one and no one believes it. It is not just because of that skilled surgeon's knife. I believe it is because what all ages are supposed to look and feel like is being redefined. I struck a bargain with Mother Nature. "I'll take care of the exercise, diet, medical self care, breast exams, DEXA scans for osteoporosis, visit my dentist regularly, use my seat belt and you let me die young at an old age."

I'm a new woman. I overcame my own propensity to beat myself up for taking care of me. The phenomenal positive difference it has made in my life and the lives of the people who have now confessed, "I did that," has made me a crusader.

Her Story Happiest Ending

There is more to this story. If anyone had asked me before my surgery if I was self-assured, I would have honestly replied, without missing a beat, "Yes." Post surgically, I realized that prior "feeling" was self-confidence. My self-confidence could be eroded by photos and videos, but my new rock solid sense of self-assurance now allows me to go out into the world knowing "I belong here." "I deserve this." "I can follow my heart and reach my goals."

Section IV

Skin Indulgence and Camouflage

"There is no cosmetic for beauty like happiness."
Lady Marguerite Blessington

18

Spa to Go

In the introduction to this book you read about a weekend with my girlfriends where we pampered ourselves and shared the comraderie that a group of women do so well. Perhaps you thought, "I'd love to do that."

You can.

Living a life of self-indulgence is not a selfish life. It is a life that, each day, is filled with choices, including the choice to take care of the most important person in your life—you.

"But my family is more important," you may argue. Perhaps you think, "Without my job I would have nothing else." Still another might say, "YOU don't understand—my day is already so packed with things to do I am lucky if I get any time to myself."

There was a time when I considered the activities I now call self-nurturing to be luxuries or, worst yet, a frivolous waste of valuable time. A long bath after I put the young members of my family to bed was the luxurious reward to a hectic day. It *never* crossed my mind to sit alone, in a contemplative state, before a fireplace in winter or on my deck in summer. That was reserved for vacations. If I had a garden, I "worked" it for landscaping purposes only.

Then, my life took another series of twists and turns that can be summed up in two words: everything changed. I chose a new way of looking at and being in the world. It didn't happen overnight, but as synchronicity would have it, one chance meeting or experience led to another. In the end I had a new mantra, "You gotta slow down to speed up."

In other words, if you don't take care of yourself nothing works as well as it can.

Now I know the pleasures of a candlelight dinner when I eat alone AND the value of a teaspoon of fragrance in a bubble bath followed by a thick, fluffy terry cloth bathrobe. I cherish regularly scheduled visits to my esthetician and a vase of fresh flowers when there's no company headed my way.

Here are some of the ways my girlfriends nurture themselves:

Dianna says: "It's all about aroma."

I have a small vial of rosemary oil by my desk. Whenever I'm fatigued and unable to concentrate I work a little of the oil into my temples and soon I'm revitalized. Dianna gave me that vial of essential oil. She believes there is something primal and instinctive about the principles of aromatherapy. She told us that legend supports the theory that every aromatic plant that has ever existed grew in the Garden of Eden.

Dianna and I rent garden spaces in a community garden near our home. I have discovered the joy of working with the earth, watching plants, then flowers, burst forth then cutting and arranging them and sharing them with neighbors. Dianna lovingly tends her garden of aromatic herbs, which she uses to make reviving and relaxing essential oils. When she began putting dried lavender in satin bags shaped to lie across a distressed forehead, she spawned a home based business that supports her quite comfortably.

The power of fragrance is primitive and primary. When it isn't overdone (there is nothing worse than a woman who wears too much perfume), it can overrule a rational brain. Dianna is an advocate of using aroma pots, incense sticks, essential oils in spritzer bottles and live plants (eucalyptus is a favorite) to scent a room and shape an environment with fragrance. Whether you put a few drops of peppermint oil in a bowl of warm water to discourage bacteria or line a closet with cedar, these small indulgences can make you feel beautiful each time you enter a room. And that's what it is all about: beauty.

A word about fragrance: a light scent is a pleasure. Too much is irritating to others. If you like fragrant lotions and cosmetics, do your friends a favor by using less when you are going to be in a crowd.

Barbara says: "Take a bubble bath."

Washing the body is one of the first things that happens to us when we are born and the last when we die. It has been depicted in ancient drawings and fine art. The routines of history's great beauties have been recorded including Cleopatra's milk baths and the vinegar baths of the Queen of Troy. Few of us would deny that a long hot shower or a soaking bath is a luxury. Add bubbles or scent to a bath, rub your body down with a loofah, use a rolled towel under your head for comfort, soak and when you let the water out your troubles will float down the drain with the water. After your bath wrap yourself in a fluffy, thick terry cloth or chenille robe (preferably warmed over a radiator or in the dryer) and ... did someone say, "stress reduction"?

Valerie says: "Give yourself the royal treatment."

Spa treatments and facials are not only good for the skin, they are good for the soul. Pampering is icing on the cake when you live a beautiful life. Valerie claims the body wraps at her favorite home town vacation site not only soften her skin but give meaning to the words "pamper yourself." Valerie has transformed the tiny bathroom in her apartment as well. The tub is lined with candles and her supplies are in inexpensive wicker baskets. There are a wide assortment of bath oils and bubbles and a tiny battery operated tape deck plus a pile of tapes on a shelf that can be reached from the tub. She's put a reflexology chart on the wall because she claims the warm water prompts her muscles to stretch sufficiently to allow her the added luxury of a self-administered foot massage. This is intended to stimulate circulation, aid natural healing and promote spiritual harmony. In other words, Valerie's bath is an event that restores her inner, as well as her outer, beauty— almost every day.

Geri says: "Try bedroom ballet."

It is easy to understand why Geri has a supple body despite her fifty plus years. She has devised her own series of daily exercises which she calls "ballet in the bedroom." When she led us through her routine we realized they really work *and* they are fun too—even if you feel as awkward as an ostrich. And, since it is never too early or too late for a little exercise...

Susan says: "Now hear this: Tina Turner and Racquel Welsh"

We're talking hair here. You may be astonished to learn that some of the most beautiful women in the world wouldn't leave their home without putting on a wig. These women do not have bad hair. They've simply discovered the pleasure of being able to look gorgeous in a minute or less. Susan has two wigs. They are cut the same. One is styled with a casual look and the other more tantalyzingly gorgeous. Is this an indulgence? She says. "Yes. I simply hate to fool with my hair. One day when I asked my hairdresser to give me a short, easy to care for cut that looked like Tina Turners or Racquel Welch's she laughed and said, 'Susan, they both wear wigs.' "

"The next day," Susan continued, "I swallowed my pride, stepped into a wig shop and the rest is history." We agreed on a future outing where, instead of sampling cosmetics or the latest book releases, we'd sample wigs. Stay tuned.

Jeannie says: "Grandchildren are everything."

If you are phobic about becoming a grandmother because it is something that is for "old" ladies, you will soon have a transforming experience. Jeannie believes that children are our angels on earth. They startle us with their simple wisdom, clear voices and loving hearts. They inspire us to be better. They teach us how to listen, to sing with joy, live with abandon and love—free of conditions. If you want to feel young again, over and over again, spend time with a grandchild, surrogate grandchild, little sister or young neighbor. You may be exhausted when they go home but you will be stunned at how the love that flows between you makes you feel alive, beautiful and blessed over and over again.

Rebecca says: "Massage is a bare necessity."

In the past, in cultures where a baby was born in a primitive environment, the first thing the attendants did after the birth was warm their hands and stroke the baby. They knew, intuitively, that we may need food and shelter to survive, but touch is a biological necessity as well as a physical pleasure. Now baby massage is a nurturing experience mothers enjoy giving their baby. Grown women, who indulge in a massage regularly, find themselves feeling nurtured "like a baby." Since everyone can benefit from human touch in a safe environment, massage is one of the more accepted ways we have of feeding skin hunger and taking care of ourselves. Researchers continue to argue whether there are any "benefits" to massage. Those who believe there isn't must not have had one. If you haven't tried a massage and aren't sure you will like it, start with a face and head massage or a hands and feet massage. Try several massage therapists and different types of massage. Learn how to give yourself a massage—especially an eye massage that can distribute nourishing blood to the eye area and decrease puffiness. You will soon discover the beauty of touch.

Other Beauty Enhancements

When attempting to discover the indulgence that works for you, start with experiences that precipitate the thought, "I can't take time for that." Change your mind by saying, "I can make time for that." Activities that appear to be frivolous are often the ones that are the best stress busters and beauty builders. Here are a few more suggestions culled from my girl friends:

✓ a hard cover book you always wanted to read
✓ a luxurious bath
✓ fresh flowers
✓ new sheets
✓ a manicure or pedicure
✓ a yoga or tai chi routine
✓ gel filled facial masks
✓ the latest "hot" exercise class (kickboxing, Pilates, hiphop)

Her Story

In between self care and the skillful hand of a competent physician is my favorite skin care specialist, my esthetician. Once a month Lori Larsen leads my stressed, talkative self into a room softened with dim lights, soft music and a bubbling fountain, forces me to remove my warmup suit and put on a skin wrap, lie on her soft double mattress table, insert my soon covered with lotion hands and feet in warmed mitts and close my eyes while she goes through a routine that includes cleansing, exfoliating, moisturizing and protecting my skin. While the creamy mask she uses works its wonders, I get a hand, foot, neck and shoulder massage that induces me to drift in and out of light sleep. An hour and a half later when her soft, cheery voice says, "Okay, you can get dressed now," I am totally relaxed and keenly aware that more than my outer self has received the royal treatment. When I dress and exit to the bright lights of the salon she greets me with a cheery, "You look beautiful!" which is, by design, echoed by everyone I pass as I exit and return to the "real" world.

19

Not So Skin Deep

Face Facts

"You don't wear cosmetics to be someone else. You wear them to be yourself...at your best...it not only expresses what's inside you, but also inspires a whole world of possibilities."

OLAY advertisement

That pretty much says it all. Makeup that is perfect for you looks natural. How many times have you met a woman who, because she desires to cover up what she believes to be a flaw, ends up with a "painted," heavy, made-up look. You have probably, also, met women who feel they can't grasp the concept of applying makeup so they decide going natural (meaning no makeup at all) is the only way to go.

There is a wonderful, happy medium that my friend, Ethel, describes as "quietly correct." It's the makeup that looks natural because the colors, shades, textures, intensity and application works with *your* skin color, *your* skin type and *your* lifestyle. You feel and look comfortable wearing it.

Ethel Harms is the consummate makeover queen. If she meets you professionally, you can expect to get a constructive but non-judgmental critique that is the product of age, wisdom and experience. You will discuss lifestyle, colors, clothes, style and more. Then she begins your makeup lesson.

After years of the same old routine my "facelift" demanded a new look. I threw out every prejudice I had about makeup and asked Ethel to pretend she just met me, "Presume I know nothing about face painting."

She agreed with one caveat, "I will not do this for you. I will teach you how to do it for yourself. Before I arrive I want you to gather every bit of makeup you have. We'll be throwing away out-dated products. Then we will streamline and update your routine. I'll bring my palette of colors in case you need one you don't already own."

In The Beginning

Step one: Examine the face.

Study bone structure, skin, hair and eye coloring to determine where dark and light colors will be used to bring balance to the face. This includes deciding which features to enhance (bright eyes, for example) and which to camouflage (a prominent nose, for example).

Step two: Choose eye shadows.

Choose eye shadow by holding a variety of colors up to your eyes. Put your mind in the framework you use when you drape a dress across your body before you consider trying it on or buying it. Ask yourself, "Which colors bring out and brighten my eye color?"

Step three: Choose lip color and blush. (These should blend.)

There are two color families: warm reds, which include coral, apricot and peach or cool reds, which include pink or the cooler bluish red some people call pink rose or plum or wine. To choose the right one for you, brush a coral/peach blush on one side of your face and a pink/wine color on the other. (It was easy to see that the pink/rose worked best for my skin tone because it blended naturally into my skin. The warm tones looked artificial.) Choose a couple of lip colors in the same color range as the blush. Then experiment to discover which looks best with your natural lip color.

Step four: Put it all together.

There are three "looks" that can be defined using makeup:

✓ a casual look (for daily life) (This is described below as a casual makeup strategy.)

✓ a professional, "finished" or polished look (for work or, in my case, for lectures or TV appearances).

✓ a glamorous evening transformation (described below)

Beyond the Beginning

Ferreting through the hundreds of makeup choices can be daunting. The best rule of thumb is to try products on before you buy them to be sure the color and texture is right for you. Since you don't know who may have sampled a product before you, be sure it has been cleaned with alcohol or that individual disposable applicators are available for you to use.

These simple guidelines can help you make selections.

Foundation: A good foundation evens your skin color and gives your complexion extra "polish."	Always check the color of your foundation at your jaw line. It should appear invisible and match your neck perfectly. Never choose a darker shade of foundation than your skin. You will look like you are wearing a mask. The formula of foundation should compliment your skin type and color. Always use a foundation that has a sunscreen of at least SPF 15.

For Dry Skin: A liquid foundation or a rich moisturizing foundation works best. Try line-diffusing formulas as your skin ages.

For Oily Skin: Try a water-based oil-free foundation or one with a powder or matte finish.

For Light Coverage (best for a casual look): Tinted moisture bases and Sport Sticks offer sheer, natural looking coverage.

For Women of Color: Until recently, unless you were "Caucasian", your makeup was blended in your bathroom. It wasn't too long ago that I watched my Caribbean friend, Susan, add plant based coloring agents like cocoa until her skin foundation matched her complexion.

Look for oil-free foundations with a warm, golden undertone. Shades of bronze, sun gold and terra-cotta are best. If your skin is a rich shade of mahogany, try foundations in warm shades with yellow undertones. Makeup lines specifically designed for dark skin tones offer a wider selection.

Concealer: A concealer hides imperfections by lightening recessed or dark areas (under the eyes, for example).	Choose from creams, liquids and sticks. The shade should be "one shade lighter" than your foundation.

Powder: A light dusting of powder "sets" your foundation. It is the key to beautifully finished makeup.	Choose a translucent powder for a "see-through" finish or one that matches your foundation in a light, medium, or dark shade. NOTE: Pressed powder in regular or oil-controlling formulas are for touch-ups only.

Eyebrow Color: Your pencil or powdered eyebrow color adds definition and color to your eyebrows.	Choose a color a shade lighter than your hair color.

Eye Shadows: These highlight, modify the shape, emphasize eye color and draw attention to your eyes.	You will need three: 1. A highlight: use a light base color in pink or beige. 2. A modifier: use a medium color that blends with your hair color. 3. An accent color: use a shade that blends with or accents your eye color.

Women of Color: Try deeply saturated warm or cool colors, deep browns and black. Avoid light pastels that look chalky on your skin.

General Rule: If you have dark eyes use deep eye shadow colors; if you have light colored eyes, choose light colored eye shadows.

Eye Pencil: Lining the eyes adds definition and makes the base of your eyelash look thicker.	Choose one of the neutral colors including gray, brown, navy, or black. (Choose black only if you have black hair.) Be sure your pencil has a soft lead so it can be smudged for a "natural" look.

Mascara: This adds fullness to your eyelashes and brightens your eyes.	Choose a color that is close to the natural color of your eyelashes. Water-soluble formulas are best because they can be removed without the excessive rubbing that may remove eyelashes or damage the eye. Replace your mascara every ninety days.

Lip Pencil: This outlines and corrects the shape of your lip line. Since it is drier than lipstick it stays on longer and keeps lipstick from "bleeding."	Choose a lip pencil in a shade as close as possible to your natural lip color.

Lipstick: A good lipstick should intensify your natural lip color and "brighten" your face.	Choose either a matte, frosted, super-frost or sheer lipstick. A general rule is: the lighter your hair color, the lighter your lipstick should be and vice versa: dark hair = dark lipstick.

✓ Matte lipsticks are usually drier and stay on longer if they have a flat finish. In a darker color, they can make full lips appear smaller.

✓ Frosted lipsticks vary in texture from a little frost to a lot of frost. The sheen will catch the light and make small lips appear larger.

✓ Super-frost lipsticks are not as flattering to aging lips because they draw attention to the lines, while a softer sheen will make the lips look moist.

✓ Sheer color lipsticks offer a soft see-through coverage for those who prefer a lighter touch of color.

Always try a lipstick on before purchasing it. Many times your skin's chemistry can cause lipsticks to change color.

Blush: This warms the skin on the cheek with soft color that can recreate a youthful look.	Choose a shade in the same color tone as your lipstick. You can choose a powder blush, a cream blush, a sheer gel or bronzer.

✓ Powder blushes provide a light dusting of color to the cheeks and are easy to control.

✓ Cream blushes provide a dewy look as your skin ages and becomes drier.

✓ A sheer gel or bronzer adds see-through color.

The rule of dark and light — Use light colors on areas that you wish to highlight, bring forward and enlarge. Use dark colors on areas that you want to downplay and reduce in size.

The rule of shiny versus matte — Finishes with shine will reflect light and enlarge an area; matte finishes will absorb light and diminish an area.

Getting Organized

Tools of the Trade:

Good tools make the difference in whether your makeup goes on smooth or sloppy. They also make the difference in how that makeup looks after you finish applying it.

Think of yourself as a fine artist. Purchase, then practice using quality brushes and applicators.

Here are the essentials:
✓ Sponge wedges – for applying foundation, cream blush and concealers
✓ Tissues – for blotting
✓ Cotton swabs – for correcting errors
✓ Pencil sharpener – to keep your pencils sharp
✓ Eyelash curler – to softly curve eyelashes
✓ Tweezers – to remove stray brow hairs (use slanted tips for maximum control when "tweezing")
✓ Sponge applicators – for smudging pencils
✓ Brushes, brushes, brushes – to apply everything
✓ Lash comb – to separate lashes

Your Brushes:
Professional makeup artists will agree that the quality, shape and selection of brushes determine how "finished" your makeup looks. If you have ever had the privilege of a makeover you know the "stylist" uses a different brush for each product that is applied. The best natural hair brushes are made of sable. In the best case scenario your supply would include:
✓ Powder brush – large, soft and full to lightly dust a powder finish to your makeup.
✓ Blush brush – medium sized for a soft application of cheek color.
✓ Eyebrow/lash comb – to groom the brows and separate the eyelashes.

✓ Eye shadow brushes (2) – one small angled brush for concentrating and blending color and one small, full brush for over-all eye shadow blending.

✓ Eyeliner brush – for cake eyeliner or for lining the eye with eye shadow.

✓ Lip brushes (2) – one for lipstick and one for camou-flaging imperfections with concealer.

Makeup works best when it is applied in a beautiful, clean, uncluttered environment. These tips can help:

✓ Use a good source of natural day light or daylight lighting. Northern light is soft and has the least amount of glare. (If you do not have good lighting in your bathroom, keep your supplies on a tray that you can move to the best location.)

✓ Never use overhead lights when applying makeup. They create too many shadows. The ideal environment for evening makeup uses a theatrical style mirror with lights surrounding the mirror. (Ask for one of these for your next birthday.)

✓ Make your makeup routine a pleasurable one. Surround yourself with beautiful tools, brushes, pretty printed cotton or silk makeup bags, wonderful wicker baskets or clear Lucite or silver boxes.

✓ Choose products and packaging that please you. If you love fragrance, surround yourself with bath products, soaps, lotions, candles and perfume all from one favorite scent.

✓ Keep everything meticulously clean.

20

The 15 Minute Facelift (Using Makeup)

For better or worse, we are often judged by first impressions. Beauty may be more than skin deep but knowing how to apply the right makeup is crucial to creating your best look. This is fun. You can be a little kid again with your brushes and pencils and tubes and, finally, the right colors to match your complexion. A good makeup application can "lift" older skin. This 15-minute routine is what I use when I want a professional look that can take me anywhere.

Start with clean hands, natural lighting (whenever possible) and your supplies close at hand.

1.   Moisturize

If you use an oil based foundation, wait a few minutes before continuing. Then, if possible, wait a few minutes so your makeup doesn't "slide."

2. Apply foundation

Dot foundation onto the forehead, cheeks, nose, and chin. Blend well with your fingers or a sponge, finishing with downward strokes to smooth facial hairs. For an extra natural effect, use a sponge that has been moistened with water. NOTE: Foundation should be "blended" by "feathering" the product at the jaw line.

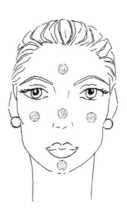

3. Apply concealer

Dot concealer (lightly) onto the dark areas of your face to bring them forward. This usually includes circles under the eyes, the inner corners of the eyes, any broken veins around the nose, the outer corners of the eyes (that can droop if gravity takes its toll) and down turned corners of the mouth. Blend with a sponge or your finger by softly tap, tap, tapping the concealer *only* into the area you want

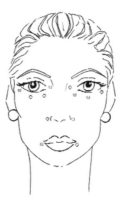

to lighten. You can use a lip brush to add concentrated color to small areas, or to cover blemishes and small imperfections (age spots and scars).

4. Apply powder

Use your large, fluffy brush to lightly dust the face with loose powder. This "sets" the foundation and concealer and gives your skin a velvet "finish." NOTE: Excess powder, which tends to settle into fine lines and wrinkles, is extremely aging. Brush, brush, brush away any excess.

5. **Apply eye shadow**

A. Apply the light "base" color of eyeshadow from the lash line to the eyebrows. This highlights the brow bone and gives lift to your face and eyelid.

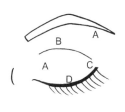

B. Apply the medium color to the eyelid at the crease line to add definition.

C. Apply the accent color from the outer corner of the eye, one-third of the way in, on the top and the bottom.

6. **Apply eyeliner**

D. Line the eyes with a soft pencil on the upper lash base from where the eyelashes start at the inner corner of the eye, to the outer corner of the eye. Line the lower lash base from the outer corner of the eye only one-third of the way in to the outside of the iris. Smudge to soften the pencil line.

7. **Apply mascara**

NOTE: If you curl your eyelashes (an instant eye opener) do it ***before*** you apply mascara. Add a light coat of mascara working from the lash base, lifting and separating the lashes. Add a second coat to the top lashes (only) for drama. If you always end up with mascara under your eyes, mascara the top lashes only. Separate any clumps with your lash comb.

8.   Pencil your brows

Your eyebrows are the frames for your eyes. A "perfectly" shaped eyebrow makes the eyes appear open and bigger. The start of the brow should line up with the inner corner of the eyes. If it doesn't, add color or thicken your brows by adding light feathered "strokes" with your eyebrow pencil. Tweeze away "stray" hairs that extend beyond that inner corner. The brow should arch at a line directly 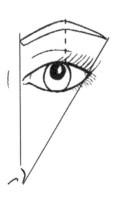 above the outside of the iris. (This is a very important part of lifting and "opening up" the eye area.) Next, to see if you need to lengthen your brow, us your pencil as a "ruler" to create an imaginary line from the base of your nose past the outer corner of your eye (see drawing). You will see where the brow should end. Tweeze away any excess hairs.

Take the pain out of plucking errant hairs by smoothing a bit of Vaseline over the area to be tweezed then placing a moist warm towel over it. Wait one minute, remove the towel and tease with ease.

9.   Lip liner

Lining your lips adds definition to the lip line which blurs as we get older. It reduces lipstick "bleeding" and adds an extra, soft coat of color when it is blended into the lips. To make your lips look fuller trace the liner slightly outside the lip line. To make the lips look thinner, line just

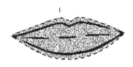

inside the lip line. Be careful. As you age corrective enlarging of the upper lip line can look artificial.

10.   Lipstick

For rich color that lasts, always use a lip brush to apply lipstick. Fill in the lips with color and blot.

11.   Blush

Using a blush brush, apply blush along the bottom of the check bone from the middle of the eye to the hairline. Smile, then cover the apples of the cheeks created by that frown turned upside down, in soft strokes of color. Brush across the brow bone in a "c" shape that connects the cheek color and eye color together for a natural glow.

12.   Check it out

To be sure you don't head to your tennis match with too much make up or the symphony performance with too little, check yourself over in a full-length mirror. You want to be sure your makeup and outfit matches your destination.

21

A Beauty Repair Kit

S.O.S. For the Eyes—Six Tips That Work

1. Dark Circles

Before applying your foundation, use a color correcting cream to neutralize and tone the areas of discoloration. They come in creams and liquids and in various colors. Here are a few favorites:

✓ Pink brightens sallow skin.
✓ Yellow covers blue and purple discoloration.
✓ Green corrects redness.

2. Puffy Eyes

✓ Apply concealer in the indentation just below the apparent fullness to lighten the "dent" and draw attention away from the puffiness. Do *not* lighten the puff itself.
✓ Focus color on the eyelid to detract from the lower eye.
✓ Do not use harsh black or dark colored eyeliner around the eye. Try a softer medium gray.
✓ Sleep with your head elevated.
✓ Avoid salty foods.

3. Wrinkled/Creepy Lids

✓ Apply an eye shadow base to the eyelids from the lash line to the brow. This will set and provide a smooth finish for applying your eye shadows.

✓ Eye bases keep your eye shadow from creasing and fading.

✓ Use matte eye shadows for more color pigment with no shine.

4. Contacts and Sensitive Eyes

✓ Use fragrance-free and water-soluble mascara that can easily be removed from the eyes without rubbing.

✓ Avoid lash-lengthening mascara that contains fibers that can cause irritation.

✓ Try a cream-to-powder eye shadow that will eliminate any chance of getting particles in your eyes.

5. Droopy/Hooded Eyelids

✓ Start your eye makeup application with an eye shadow base.

✓ There are two approaches to uplifting droopy eyelids:

  i. Begin modifying the look of your eye by lining the outer 1/3 of the eye lifting the line slightly at the corner. Smudge the line. Apply your medium color eye shadow to the fullness of the lid above the crease line.

  ii. The second is to line the lower 1/3 of the eye at the outer corner with a light to medium taupe pencil and extend the line, lifting slightly, to the crease. At this point, draw a crease with your pencil 2/3 of the way toward the inner corner of the eye, following the natural shape of the eye.

✓ Do not line the eyelid.

✓ Smudge the pencil and blend the line with your medium colored shadow.

You have just performed "eyelid surgery" with makeup.

6.   Makeup For Glasses

If you are nearsighted- your glasses will make your eyes look smaller. Play up your eyes with light colors and sheen that will bring them forward and enlarge them. If you are farsighted – these lenses will magnify the size of your eye. Use less makeup in soft subtle colors. Go easy on the mascara.

* A low bridge on your glasses will shorten your nose and a high bridge will lengthen your nose.

* Choose your frames in a color that picks up your hair color, your eye color or your skin tone.

Lip Service

To prevent lipstick from vanishing before you want it to:

✓ Layer your lipstick by applying it with a brush, blotting and reapplying.

✓ Outline your lips and fill them in with the pencil as the first layer of color.

✓ Try a lip base product that neutralizes lip tone and keeps lipstick from feathering and fading.

✓ Apply a lipstick sealer over your lipstick. This product does for lips what clear nail polish does for your finger-nails.

To prevent lipstick from bleeding:

✓ Use concealer all around your mouth and powder lightly before applying lip color.

✓ Line with a lip pencil to prevent feathering and blot.

✓ Use a lip primer and a lip sealer.

To remedy lip lines:
- ✓ Try a product that softens and plumps the lips.
- ✓ Invest in collagen injections. (a temporary fix - see page 116)
- ✓ Invest in a peel around the lips. (a permanent fix – see page 112)

To relieve dry, chapped lips:
- ✓ Use a lip pumice with tiny granules to exfoliate the lips and peel away the dry, dead skin.
- ✓ Condition and protect the lips with a moisture and sunscreen stick to keep them moist before applying lipstick.
- ✓ Use a moisturizing lipstick at all times if you have dry lips.

To camouflage drooping lips:
- ✓ Use foundation all around the lips.
- ✓ Dot concealer at the down-turned corners of the mouth to lighten the shadows. (See the 15-minute facelift with makeup.)
- ✓ Slightly correct the lips as you line them by lifting the corners.

To flatter teeth:
- ✓ If your teeth have a gray tinge – choose a warm bronze or copper lipstick.
- ✓ If you have yellow teeth – choose blue-based shades of red, cranberry and wine.

About Facial Hair:
Around menopause, just as the hair on your scalp begins to thin, a new crop of errant hard, white, wiry hairs may burst

forth from your chin and eyebrows. My friend, Joanne's hubby calls these wayward protrusions his "lucky hairs." Girlfriends disagree. Make a pack with yours that you will tell one another when you spot wild hair that they have missed plucking. You can also:

✓ Try a depilatory cream that is formulated for faces only;

✓ Consider a waxing kit to keep you smoother longer;

✓ Visit your local esthetician's salon for a professional waxing experience;

✓ Electrolysis uses a fine needle to probe the hair follicle with a very low electric current. This destroys the hair. Be sure the technician is qualified;

✓ The FDA has approved laser treatment for hair removal. It works. Use caution in choosing a clinic.

NOTE: Women of color should not have laser treatments as it can effect the color pigmentation of the skin.

22

Mature Is Not a Dirty Word

Her Story

In 1958, I was infatuated with everything about musical theater. In an effort to reconnect with me after my first year at college, my mother took me to New York City to visit friends, shop, tour art museums and "see some shows." New York musical theater was thriving and each show had a memorable story, songs and dancing. Two of those shows featured songs I've sung over and over throughout my life — for myself and for my children. Rodgers and Hammerstein's "I Enjoy Being A Girl," sung by the female lead in Flower Drum Song, and Leonard Bernstein's "I Feel Pretty," sung by the female lead in West Side Story, elegantly capture the joys of personal beauty from the inside out and the outside in. Each girl is preparing for a date with her boy friend. The outfit, hair and makeup for each are pretty, but it is the glow of an inner beauty that shines on their faces and rings true to us, even in their voices. It is a poignant example that how we feel about ourselves affects every aspect of our experience.

Posture Perfect

"Stand up straight." "Suck in your tummy." The traditional dictates of good posture are hard to forget. As we age, too many of us slump. Frighteningly, this is rarely about poor posture. It is, more often, about osteoporosis. Fifty percent of all women over age 50 will have an osteoporosis based fracture before they die. Not all of these will occur because of a fall. A majority will be spontaneous fractures of the spine which lead to the dreaded dowager's hump we believe is a characteristic of "old" women. It's not. If you want to stand tall, get smart and make strong bones. Exercise regularly (see Chapter 23), drink your milk and supplement with calcium. If you are diagnosed with osteoporosis, use one of the revolutionary drugs in the bisphosphonate category like Actonel, the newest drug to repair and restore bone mass.

There are many advantages to aging but, for most women, the body shifts that occur isn't one of them. For some this is only about a loss of skin elasticity, but for others there is, also, what health experts call "creeping obesity." When this happens a woman, even a fit woman, may look at herself in the mirror, realize she's gained a few pounds she is *sure* she can lose and slip into big, boxy shirts, elastic waist pants and baggy dresses. These are comfortable clothes that she believes "hides" everything. Fashion experts tell us this isn't true. Our eyes may see camouflage but these styles make you look BIGGER.

Instead of covering up, first, think tall. Elegant women look great because their posture lengthens their look. Once you "stand tall" updating your wardrobe can add to this long look even if you are five feet tall. The secret is choosing simple design lines using more structured classic fabrics like cotton, linen and wool.

Beyond this the rule of thumb is "less is more." This doesn't mean less effort. Here is your work order: Go to your

closet and get rid of anything that emphasizes busts that are heavier thanks to
added weight or hormone replacement
therapy. To look pounds thinner no
matter what size you are, keep clothes that
fit you well and define the figure you are
blessed with. If you have a waist,
emphasize it with a belt. If your waist is
past history, emphasize necklines. (See the
before and after pictures.)

Remember, too, that looking great
is not about looking young. It is about
emphasizing your assets, minimizing your
liabilities and focusing on your unique-
ness and vitality. Most of all it is about
that out-the-door ability to exemplify
(from the inside out) the meaning of
those memorable Broadway songs, "I Feel
Pretty" and "I Enjoy Being A Girl."

A Word About Wardrobe

Here is some more good "girlfriend"
advice for easy to implement "lifting and
slimming" ideas:

- ✓ Use turned-up collars to create a
  vertical, slimming line and "pizzazz."
- ✓ Add shoulder pads for a straight,
  strong, youthful shoulder line.
- ✓ Open necklines add length to the
  upper torso.
- ✓ A vest or lightweight shirt-jacket will
  conceal a protruding tummy.

B
E
F
O
R
E

A
F
T
E
R

✓ Add a belt under a jacket to give the illusion of a waistline.

✓ Wear narrow legged trousers for a slimming look.

✓ Wear shoes that have (at least) a one inch heel to lengthen and slim the leg.

✓ Be sure your clothes are updated, freshly pressed and spotless. (This is where you make a pact with your best friend to promise to exchange warnings when an outfit has "seen its day.")

✓ And *the best advice of all,* see a good hair stylist. A new haircut with diagonal lines that "lift" and draw attention away from the jawline will do wonders for your new look. I can just see you now, doing that double take as you walk by a mirror.

Tips, Tips and More Tips

Hair Color

In this day and age of soft hair color choices and color weaving a woman does not have to live with gray hair unless it is flattering. Work with a trusted colorist to select hair coloring that is flattering to your skin tone. Try color weaving with highlights (lighter strands) and lowlights (darker strands) for a natural look. Or, have some highlights added to your existing color to lift and focus attention above the brow line.

Smile (as often as possible)!

Whiten your teeth. It's amazing how it brightens your whole face! A simple tray that creates a mold of your teeth, then is filled with a whitening gel is easy to use for at-home bleaching. Check with your dentist to see if she/he has other options.

Hands Down

Our hands constantly take a beating! We expose them to countless washings, household cleaners, gardening, paper, fabrics and much, much more. Then we expose them to the elements. They need special treatments after what they go through in a normal day. Give your hands the same care that you give to the skin on your face. Use exfoliating or hydrating masks, your alpha hydroxy cream and daytime moisturizer with an SPF15 to keep hands looking healthy.

Treat your hands to manicures. The most youthful looking manicures feature shorter nails trimmed in a slightly oval shape that follows the natural nail line. Unless you are going to a party or want to show off your hands, use soft nail colors. Choose a nail color in a soft pink or white.

Get Control of Yourself

Invest in good, supporting, undergarments. The difference a good bra makes is incredible. Have your bra fitted by an expert (usually available at most stores, or when there are special promotions). Choose a bra to lift or to minimize and make sure that the shoulder straps are comfortable. Take the time to browse through the lingerie department of your favorite store. Try on some of the many body shapers, waist cinchers and girdles that control and smooth those lumps and bumps. You'll feel and look much better in your clothes.

Section V

Under Your Skin

"If spot reducing worked, people who chew gum would have skinny faces."
Charles Kuntzelman

23

Smart Exercise

Exercise is king when it comes to providing all the organs of the body with the continual supply of oxygen-rich blood and the nutrients that assure peak performance. Despite what you may read or hear elsewhere, exercise is also the best way to purify (remove toxins from) your body. Because exercise is the best way to move anything through your body it is also the best way to transfer other wastes to the outside of your body via your skin. That is why skin is a primary beneficiary of an active lifestyle.

Exercise requires energy and energy production creates heat. The tiny blood vessels in the dermis expand to get rid of the heat. That is why, if your skin is light, you see it turn rosy-red when you exercise. That heat also triggers the sweat glands to produce sweat which moves to the top layer of the skin to cool the body when it evaporates. Perspiration is also a healthy way for your skin to bathe itself and move internal wastes outside the body. Meanwhile, that heat also affects bacteria inside and outside the skin. Most of them cannot withstand the change in temperature exercise produces so they perish.

Exercise also keeps the subcutaneous (under the skin) fat at the optimum thickness to protect underlying organs. It also keeps the muscles under your skin fit to give the outside of your body, including facial skin, looking "firm."

If you already have an exercise strategy in place, it isn't necessary to sell you on the benefits. If exercise has not been a part of your lifestyle, the encouragement to exercise may have little meaning for you until you know:

✓ What's the best kind of exercise?
✓ How do you begin?
✓ How do I get fit fast?

Workout Savy

Exercise is so beneficial to our physical, mental, social, emotional and spiritual health that if it could be packaged in a pill it would be prescribed for everyone alive.

What's the Best Kind of Exercise?

The best kind of exercise is the one you will do on a regular basis. There is currently a movement by the Surgeon General's office to get couch potatoes on their feet by encouraging "anything that accumulatively lasts 30 minutes a day." It is a good place to start, but if you want to bring a healthy, reborn look to your skin, you've got to ***MOVE!***

If you enjoyed an active lifestyle at any earlier time in your life, chances are you will still enjoy the activities you did "back then." If not, consider fitness walking. Since I believe that fitness is about more than a workout, I believe that in addition to the physical benefits of this activity, walking clears your mind so you can work through the mental challenges that come your way. When walking wisdom includes the company of a friend or group of friends, it is also good for your social health. It's hard to bury your head under the covers or in your work when your integrity demands you keep a commitment to share a walking experience.

Emotionally, walking is a sanity saver. No matter what is happening in your life, chances are a walk can pep you up or calm you down. Last, but certainly not least, are the spiritual aspects of communing with nature when an outdoor walk, rain or shine, is part of your fitness program. It is, for me, in movement, that I reconnect with that part of me that knows all is right with the world. Maybe it's the deep breathing an invigorating walk precipitates. Maybe it is the blood flow triggered by muscles that thrive when pushed beyond day to day activity. Maybe it is ... it doesn't matter. Walking is beauty.

How Do I Begin?

You begin an exercise program by putting on a pair of sturdy shoes and walking out the door (and beyond) or donning your workout gear and moving your body through the door of the nearest athletic facility to an exercise machine or exercise class. For more specifics, there are excellent exercise self-help books listed in the resource section of this book. Nevertheless, my lengthy career in fitness compels me to give you the basic background that can help you get started.

Exercise 101

There are two "kinds" of exercise. The first, aerobic, is the one that pushes you sufficiently to do some deep breathing. Aerobic means air and air means oxygen. You have already learned that all cells, including those in your skin, require a healthy dose of oxygen to do their job.

Exercise that requires oxygen is also exercise that burns stored body fat. Since, for most women, attaining a healthy weight is part of what keeps us looking and feeling beautiful, fat burning exercise is the place to start.

For the purpose of skin vitality I recommend one of the following aerobic (fat burning) exercises:

✓ cycling
✓ dancing
✓ hiking
✓ jogging
✓ martial arts

✓ rebounding
✓ swimming/water aerobics
✓ walking, jogging, running
✓ yoga—especially astanga yoga

You may be surprised that I didn't list tennis, golf or volleyball. These are a few of the activities that fit in the other exercise category, anaerobic exercise.

You are "doing" anaerobic exercise when you engage in activities that require short bursts and spurts of activity. In addition to the racket sports or other activities where you work hard, then rest, strength training or weight lifting requires this same kind of intensity. You lift a weight until the group of muscles you are using start to feel tired. That is a signal to stop that movement. Next, you lift that, or another, weight in a new direction until that muscle group gets tired. Exercising all your muscle groups this way forces them to rely on fuels that don't require oxygen.

Since oxygen is so important to cell metabolism you might think anaerobic exercise isn't important. That is not true. It is the best way to train the muscles to use fat when the exercise is over to repair the micro-tears that make more muscle — this increases your metabolism. It also engages more muscle fibers anytime you move, so your metabolism is kicked up a notch every time you do anything that requires physical activity.

Smart Women, Strong Bones

Weight lifting (also called strength training) is important for another reason. It makes your bones STRONG and MAXIMIZES BONE MASS. This important benefit can help prevent osteoporosis, a life threatening disease. Fifty percent of women over age 50 have osteoporosis but don't know it. Unless they exercise regularly (and take a calcium supplement), they are primary candidates for a broken bone if they fall. A fall isn't necessary to have a broken bone. A sudden movement can be the source of a spontaneous spinal fracture that can precipitate a posture-damaging dowager's hump. Aerobic exercise, especially the activities that are done on a hard surface, also support the strong bones that are the framework for our skin.

In short, if you combine an aerobic and anaerobic exercise during your workout, you are guaranteed to do what counts most for glowing skin and setting the stage for the inner life that makes us glow from the inside out.

Getting Fit

When you develop your exercise program it is important to rely on principles of exercise that professionals have used for years. There is an acronym that makes this easy to understand. It's FIT where:

F = frequency, or how often you exercise
I = intensity, or how hard you exercise
T = time, or how long you exercise

You have a choice to:
1.   Exercise frequently, but not hard or for very long;
2.   Exercise with "intensity," so you don't have to exercise as often or as long;

3. Exercise for a long time so you don't have to exercise as often or as hard.

Of course, you can combine these three variables in various ways. In fact, your results will be based on how many of the variables are brought into play. If you exercise often, hard and for long periods of time you are more prone to injury. If you exercise rarely, at a low intensity and for short periods of time, it will be a long time before you see results. As in most things, moderation is the best course of action.

Some exercise specialists add a second T (for technique) to describe the kind of exercise you choose. For vibrant skin I prefer walking, dancing, playing tennis, climbing stairs or anything else that creates an impact on a floor, stair, track or street surface.

If you exercise at this frequency	Your Intensity will be	The suggested amount of Time of the exercise session	Suggested Technique
2–3 x day	low to moderate	10–15 minutes	walk, low impact aerobics, exercise machine
Daily	moderate to hard	30–40 minutes	jog/run, step aerobics
Daily	low to moderate	60–90 minutes	walk

How Do I Get Fit Fast?

The ability to get fit fast (and it is possible) is nature's best motivation to continue. To do so, you *have* to exercise on a regular basis. One of the most exciting pieces of research to emerge in recent years reveals that when we *take 10,000 steps* every day we have taken care of the most basic of fitness principles, "just move."

You may think that it's no big deal to *take 10,000 steps a day*. But, a conscious review of the way we live our lives brings understanding to the increased disease state we women suffer if we choose inactivity. The typical American walks about 1500 steps a day. We sit at computers. We drive cars wherever we want and need to go. We park as close as possible to our destinations. We rely on technical equipment and labor saving devices that require only a push of the button rather than the push of an arm or a leg.

If you want to get fit fast, alternate aerobic and anaerobic activity. It is easy to do if walking is your exercise choice. After you warm up, walk at a pace that allows you to talk to your companion. Then, push your intensity to a level where you get slightly out of breath. Slow down until the conversation takes on a normal rhythm, then push yourself again. This technique is called interval training. If you think this sounds like something a competitive athlete would do, you are right. It *is* the way they take their training to higher and higher levels. No matter where you are in your fitness program, pushing yourself a little harder at regular intervals during your workout will help you burn more fat during and after your activity *and* give you the "all over your body" benefits that are important for a beautiful and long life.

Last but Not Least

Back in the sleepy Seventies, the "softer" side of fitness was the hobbyhorse of New Agers and rock stars with travelling gurus. Now, exercise recommendations that include, "try yoga, pilates and tai chi" and focus on flexibility, coordination, balance and variety are mainstream. That is because living a beautiful life is not about running marathons or acquiring a buff body. It is about being able to lift bags of groceries and the packages life brings us, to stretch our backs and our mind, to coordinate our footwork and our life's work. It is about being able to prevent physical falls by balancing on one foot and preventing emotional falls by bringing balance to the path we negotiate through the road map of life.

Last but not least, lifetime fitness is about variety. In the exercise world varying your activity is called cross conditioning. It is designed to bring spice to your workout, prevent injury and allow you to exercise anywhere, despite less than perfect weather patterns. In the real world, variety is the spice of life.

Fitness is more than a workout, it's a lifestyle. Like beauty, it is more than skin deep. It is so beneficial to our physical, mental, social, emotional and spiritual health that if it could be packaged in a pill it would be prescribed for EVERYONE.

Exercise Guidelines

1. **Find an exercise you enjoy.** Better yet, find several exercises you enjoy—or at least find tolerable. That is the only way to assure you'll keep coming back for more. Mentally, return to your childhood to remember what activities you enjoyed. Repeat them now, and your heart will sing again. When, as

an adult, I got on a bicycle with upright handle-bars, similar to those on the bike I had when I was young, I rediscovered a passion for cycling I'd never experienced stooped over on the touring bicycle I'd used for years.

2. **Start slowly.** This guideline is about injury prevention. Rome wasn't built in a day and a fit, strong, beautiful body isn't either. Your effort should progress until you are moving longer, more often, and with sufficient intensity to fortify every aspect of a beautiful life.

3. **Be patient.** Adults are so impatient. We spend a lot of time teaching children patience, then neglect the lesson ourselves. Instead of attempting to whip yourself into shape in a few short weeks, progress slowly. This prevents injury and will leave you thinking, "Hmmm ... that wasn't so bad; maybe tomorrow I'll go a little farther or faster or longer."

4. **Exercise often.** Consistency gives you the real benefits of exercise. Essentially, you remind your muscles this activity is going to happen on a regular basis so they become more efficient at utilizing stored fuel. If you are an absolute beginner, you're better off exercising for short periods of time several times a day. If this doesn't work for you, exercise for at least 20-30 minutes, a minimum of four times a week. You can sustain a current fitness level working out three times a week, but you will need to exercise more often to whip your body into beautiful shape.

5. **Do ANYTHING** that will help you stick with your program. Set short- and long-term goals that will motivate you, not discourage you. Some people like the structure of a planned program, or the record keeping that helps them to measure their goals. Others like to go with the flow and decide what they are going to do, and when, on a daily basis.

How To Choose A Personal Trainer.

A good personal trainer needs the same qualities as a good friend: someone you respect who brings out the best in you, knows when to push for more and when to lay off.

The first sign of expertise is certification from the American College of Sports Medicine (http://www.acsm.org) or the American Council on Exercise (http://www.acefitness.org). Many trainers also have a degree from an accredited university in exercise physiology, human movement, anatomy, kinesiology or physical education. To narrow the search, ask friends or fitness professionals for referrals. Be sure you choose someone who specializes in clients similar to you or those who train people with your specific fitness goals.

Once you're satisfied with the credentials, talk with the trainer about your goals and how they can best be met. Think carefully about the answers — if you have a similar approach, keep talking; if you feel like your headed back to high school physical education, run the other way.

24

Smart Eating

How We Got To Today

Good nutrition used to be easy. There really wasn't much to think about since everything was good for you. Oh! I forgot to tell you. I was talking about the beginning of the last century, before vitamins were discovered or the link between diet and disease had been established. Women shopped at grocery stores not supermarkets. Their choices did not include, to name a few, packaged foods, fat and sugar substitutes, lowfat versions of anything or "natural" foods. The perfect meal was meat plus three: a yellow vegetable, a green vegetable and a starch like potato or rice. Milk was the ideal drink, bread was slathered with butter, and dessert was homemade pie, cake or cookies with an occasional scoop of homemade ice cream.

Fast forward to the twenty-first century. We are facing diet-information overload. Vegetarianism and the soy based foods that used to be the mainstay for people with beads and Birkenstocks, have gone mainstream. Food consciousness accompanies social activism and spiritual growth. Scientists discovered that more than 10,000 "nutrients" are present in foods and, thanks to sloppy legislation, there has been an explosion of "health-enhancing" megavitamins, magic pills and potions. These are packaged and sold by savvy entrepreneurs at exorbitant costs to not-yet-savvy people who sincerely want good health. Weight loss plans have been named after cities, movie stars and hospitals. Anyone with a diet book to pitch will tell you that his or her strategy for eliminating food groups, eating for your blood type and manipulating calories so they are high or low in protein, carbohydrate or fat is the only way to go. Despite food options that allow us to eat a better and more varied diet than any other time in history, we continue to sit on our butts, but worry about depleted soil, pesticides and genetically engineered foods.

Okay. I'll get off my soap box now and get on with the good stuff.

Eating for Your Body

Chocolate cake and Twinkies may be junk food to you, but if you were stranded on a desert island they could mean the difference between life and death for at least a few days. You may scorn sugar and fat, but the fact they often provide you with extra calories you don't need doesn't make them bad.

Foods that are highly touted for being "nutritious" often contain fewer nutrients than some fairly decent foods that we tend to sneer at. A fast-food hamburger, for instance, has more nutrients than Mother Nature's fresh-picked apple. Fruit juices in boxes are nothing more than a smattering of vitamins in a solution of sugar and water. Their use to satisfy a child's thirst, instead of milk, set the stage for one of the most prolific women-killers of all time, osteoporosis.

So, let's get something straight: Foods are not good *or* bad—foods are good *and* bad. Every food has some good stuff and some bad stuff. The question that requires resolution is what choice will you make to fuel your body and your skin from the inside out?

This Is the Truth

I used to follow dietitians around in an attempt to find out how to make wise food choices. There were so many diverse guidelines about which fat was better or worse for you (and your skin), how much sugar and salt and cholesterol we should or shouldn't eat, and the percentage of the macronutrients (fat, carbohydrate and protein) I needed every day, I realized I needed a full time nutritionist and cook to make sense of it all.

I shifted my perspective and soon discovered the advice all of them *agreed* upon was steeped in science that determined which diet was best for long term longevity. The guidelines are so simple and filled with common sense they don't get much attention. Eat a diet that is:

✓ lower in fat (especially saturated animal fats)
✓ lower in sugar (this is about added sugars)
✓ higher in fiber (this is about complex carbohydrates)
✓ balanced and varied (includes all the food groups)
✓ sufficient in calories (this can be calculated)

These generate a menu that will provide fuel for good health, a realistic weight (especially if you exercise), vibrant and glowing skin and the inner resources to choose wisely each time you make a new food choice.

Putting the Guidelines to Work

The end of this chapter includes strategies to lower dietary fat, a list of ways sugars can be disguised on food labels and the best food choices when you want to increase dietary complex carbohydrates (and the antioxidants that reside in them). The balance and variety perspective can be managed in two ways: use of the U. S. Government Food Pyramid or (in my humble opinion) a Smart Eating Food Chart that is illustrated in my book, *Smart Eating.* If you visit my web site: http://www.rondagates.com, you will find a calculator that will tell you exactly how many calories you need to eat every day.

Eating for Your Skin

Beyond the basic guidelines on the previous page, research shows that foods high in antioxidants are the best choices to prevent and repair body damage.

Antioxidants are abundant in the following foods:
✓ the darkest green, yellow, and orange vegetables and fruits including spinach, kale, orange squash, bell peppers, avocado, cantaloupe, honeydew melon;
✓ citrus fruit including pineapple, tomatoes, berries;
✓ nuts and seeds (limit amounts; they are high in fat);
✓ salmon, halibut (fish that have omega oils).

In chapter thirteen you learned how antioxidants work and which ones have been shown to be useful for skin care. Now there is more on the horizon. We are also learning about the benefits of a sister nutrient to the antioxidants called phytochemicals. Phytochemicals are chemicals that exist naturally in all plants (*phyto* comes from the Greek word for plant). Now, more and more of these are being isolated from foods (garlic, soybeans, licorice root, broccoli, carrots and tomatoes are just a few of the many foods being pulled apart and examined by scientists).

There may be 10,000 phytochemicals in tomatoes alone.

Today, nutrition's scavenger hunt is focused on finding ways to extract these healthful elements from the foods we may not want to eat and put them, sometimes in megadoses, into supplements and foods we do want to eat. For example, if a little bit of beta-carotene that is in a carrot is good for you, wouldn't a lot of beta-carotene in your corn flakes be better?

When antioxidants and phytochemicals are put into supplements they are called nutraceuticals, putting them somewhere between nutrients and pharmaceuticals.

There is some disappointing news. It appears these potent nutrients in food don't make it to the visible, *outer* epidermis. Nevertheless, hitting skin from the inside out is a wise decision because what happens inside is a building block for your skin's appearance.

Beyond that, instead of worrying about whether individual nutrients do or don't work or spending a fortune to buy them in pill form, mix and match nutraceuticals, phytochem-icals, and the other vitamins and minerals that make a beautiful you by going back to the guidelines on page 179. Eat less high fat meat and dairy products and eat more whole grains, fresh fruits and vegetables. Limit packaged foods and foods that have added sugar and fat and eat more whole grains, fruits and vegetables.

Be sure to consult your doctor or a dietitian before you take extra doses of those pills and potions, especially if you are taking a prescription drug.

Sugars can be disguised on package labels when they are called:

brown sugar	levulose
cane sugar	maltose
confectioner sugar	mannitol
corn sweetener	maple syrup
corn syrup	molasses
dextrin	"raw" sugar
dextrose	refined sugar
fructose	sorbitol
glucose	sucrose (table sugar)
hexitol	turbinado sugar
honey	xylitol
invert sugar	

Fat Busters!

Instead of	Use
1 cup whole milk	1 cup of 2% milk or
	1% milk or
	skim milk
1 cup of chocolate milk	1 cup of skim chocolate milk
2 T light cream	2 T half and half
	2 T whole milk
1 T butter/margarine	1 T whipped butter or
	diet margarine or
	cream cheese or
	jam or jelly
2 T sour cream	2 T reduced fat sour cream or
	low fat yogurt
2 T cream cheese	2 T Neufchatel cheese
	apple butter
2 oz. cheddar cheese	3 oz. Swiss cheese or
	part skim mozzarella or
	reduced-fat cheddar cheese
1/2 cup cottage cheese	1/2 cup of 2% lowfat cottage
	cheese or
	1% lowfat cottage cheese
1/4 cup ricotta cheese	1/4 cup part skim ricotta cheese
	2% lowfat cottage cheese
	1% lowfat cottage cheese
1 sweet roll	1 English muffin
	3 in. corn muffin
	3 in. bran muffin
1 oz. granola	1 oz. Grape-Nuts
3 egg omelet with cheese	2 egg omelet with red and
	green peppers
	2 poached eggs
2 oz. sausage	2 oz. lean sausage

Instead of	Use
2 slices thin bacon	1 slice Canadian bacon
1 cup cream soup	1 cup broth-based soup
2 slices thin pizza with meat/cheese	2 slices thin pizza with vegetables
3 oz. oil packed tuna	3 oz. water packed tuna
a tuna salad sandwich	a turkey sandwich with 1 tsp. mayonnaise
a bologna sandwich	a lean cold cut sandwich
1 serving French fries	a baked potato with 1 T sour cream
1 oz. bag potato chips	pretzels popcorn
2 T blue cheese salad dressing	2 T reduced calorie dressing or flavored vinegars
1 T mayonnaise	1 T light mayonnaise
1/2 cup Hagen Daz	1/2 cup regular ice cream
1/2 cup regular ice cream	1/2 cup frozen yogurt or ice milk
12 oz. milk shake	1 scoop ice cream cone
1 oz. chocolate bar	several pieces of hard candy
1 oz. peanuts.	1 oz. raisins

To manage your weight, lower the fat and sugar
in your diet and manage food portions. Use these "visuals"
as reminders:

3 oz. meat, poultry or fish = deck of playing cards or audio
  cassette tape
1 oz. of meat, poultry or fish = matchbook
1 cup of fruit or yogurt = baseball
1/2 cup of chopped vegetables = 3 regular ice cubes
1 medium potato = computer mouse
1 cup potatoes, rice or pasta = a tennis ball
1 standard bagel = hockey puck
1 cup chopped fresh leafy greens = 4 lettuce leaves
2 T peanut butter = golf ball
1 oz cheese = four dice or a tube of lipstick or one ping
  pong ball
1 slice of cheese = 3.5 inch computer disk
1/2 cup of cooked vegetables = 6 asparagus spears or 7-8
  baby carrots or 1 ear of corn or 3 spears of broccoli

25

Smart Weight Management

I've said it before and I'll say it again. Crash diets don't work. When it comes to managing your weight, your best course of action is to manage portion control and adopt a smart exercise program. Then, watch what happens to your body. After years helping people manage their weight here are the factors I believe you need to know.

1.   You have to eat enough calories. If you know what your weight goal is, it is possible to compute how many calories *you* need to eat every day. (This can be calculated for you if you visit my web site: http://www.rondagates.com.) Most women eat too few calories. Others eat too many, rarely choose them wisely, gain weight, then eat too few again. When your body doesn't get the calories and nutrients it needs it must make choices. Will it keep your skin vibrant or will it keep your eyes blinking, your brain functioning or the other millions of needs that supercede the needs of your skin. Science reveals the truth: if you yo-yo

diet or have eating disorders you won't have a healthy body or healthy skin.

2.   Longevity is directly related to lifestyle habits including the choices we make about what we do and don't eat. Research shows that the guidelines in the Smart Eating chapter include the principles that predispose you to a healthy adulthood.

The same applies to weight management. People who sell diet books will tell you differently, but there are years and years of research that validate you must balance the protein, carbohydrate and fat that provides those calories in a way that assures you get all the vitamins and minerals your body needs. This will help you live a long and healthy life, provide energy, keep your mind alert, help you make wise decisions *and* continue to build and repair tissue (including skin).

3.   You need some protein but not too much. Only protein builds and repairs tissue. Ten to fifteen percent of that calorie calculation in item 1. needs to be protein. Eat more and your body will excrete it. Eat less and your body chooses which tissues it will and will not repair today.

4.   Calories count. Currently, popular crash diets are low in calories (why you lose weight) and low in carbohydrates. The premise for the latter strategy is that if you don't eat lots of carbohydrates (which break down into the body's usable form, glucose) your body will convert stored body fat to glucose.

That's only partly true. Before your fat cells release that (stored) grease, days after the diet is started, your body converts stored protein, not fat, to glucose via a process known as gluconeogenesis (the making of new sugar). That means that within hours of depriving your body of calories, especially carbohydrate calories, your body must make a choice as to whether the protein is going to be used to rebuild tissues or to supply glucose to feed your brain and muscles. High protein diets promise the increased protein intake will overcome this possibility. It makes logical sense but the body works in a biochemically, not intellectually, logical way.

5. Last but not least, crash dieting almost always ultimately fails. More than 98% of people who lose 20 pounds gain that weight back—and more. Your body's skin suit stretches, then shrinks, stretches bigger, then shrinks. Soon you have stretch marks and skin that sags more than it should. It is not a pretty picture.

Skin Savvy
Prolonged fasting or juice fasts are toxin-producing to the skin.

A few extra pounds can plump skin and make it smoother. That is why if you have been overweight for a long period of time then lose the weight your skin may continue to sag.

The goal is to determine what weight you can achieve and maintain for a lifetime. That includes creating a diet to support that weight which doesn't deprive you of the foods that nurture as well as nourish you. Add moderate exercise and stick to your program for a long time and your body will weigh the assets and liabilities of your lifestyle and adjust itself accordingly. Diet and your skin will get sallow. Eat moderately, but with pleasure and in harmony with your inner self, and your body and skin will radiate.

Send $2 with your name and address to LIFESTYLES by Ronda Gates, PO Box 974, Lake Oswego, OR 97034, and you will receive, by return mail, a refrigerator size poster that will make it surprisingly easy to adopt the strategies in the last three chapters.

26

A Word About Water

An Urban Legend

When I was writing the book, *Smart Eating,* my co-author and I split chapter assignments. I chose "Do I Need To Drink Water?" While researching the answer, I discovered that the challenge to drink 6-8 glasses of water a day is the result of a misinterpretation of recommended daily allowances for water published by the National Academy of Sciences in 1945. It read:

"A suitable allowance of water for adults is 2.5 liters (83 ounces) daily in most instances. An ordinary standard for diverse people is one milliliter for each calorie of food. *Most of this quantity is contained in prepared foods.*"

Somehow, the final sentence was lost in the translation. The eight-glass-a-day movement picked up momentum in 1967 with the publication of *The Doctor's Quick Weight Loss Diet,* which sold more than 12 million copies.

Just because a recommendation turns out to be an urban legend doesn't mean the advice is bad. Drinking lots of water and eating food that has a lot of water incorporated into its preparation helps keep skin hydrated and moist and gives it a more supple appearance. Water helps the body recover from the dehydrating effects of hot water, exercise, alcohol or a high-in-salt diet and flushes cellular wastes more efficiently. It gives our internal organs a workout and maintains the sixty percent of our body weight that is water. The brain is also bathed in water (content seventy-five percent) so, I believe, it is a key factor in helping us think clearly about skin care and everything else.

Humans are funny. We wean babies from a bottle, then when they grow up tell them how important it is to carry one again. The rise in mass marketing of bottled water is a good thing. It means that a pick-me-up, which is much better for you and your skin than a caffeine-laden cup of coffee or alcoholic thirst quencher, is within easy reach. When you quench your thirst with a chemical or sugar-laden drink, pouring it over a glass full of ice, or alternating it with a glass of water, will help prevent you from retaining fluid.

If you are drinking too much water you know it because you are spending all your time ferreting out the location of the rest room in every building you enter. If you aren't drinking enough water you may experience cramped toes or a headache long before you get thirsty, a signal that you are seriously dehydrated.

I love beautiful jewelry but believe that water, used inside and out, is a better present for your skin than a sapphire bracelet. It is the secret weapon for all great beauties.

As for the chapter in that book. Do I need to drink water? The answer is YES!

Section VI

Beyond Skin –
The Invisible Factors

"You've got to get up every morning with a smile on your face and show the world all the love in your heart. Then people are going to treat you better. You're going to find, yes you will, that you're beautiful as you feel."

Carol King

27

"Don't Worry, Be Happy"

Her Story

Humans are fascinating. What could be more intriguing than learning that a positive experience for one person is a negative one for someone else. Public speaking is a good example. Most people are severely stressed if they have to speak to a large audience. Just the thought of it kicks catecholamines, potent body chemicals, into action. Soon that part of the nervous system over which we have no direct voluntary control triggers a cascade of physiological changes that marshal the body to readiness. Heart rate, blood pressure and mucle tension (designed to help us escape) rise sharply; the stomach and intestines become less active; blood sugar rises. This physical turmoil generally goes along with a psychological response: racing thoughts, anxiety and, for some, panic.

I am not stressed by public speaking. If there is a sense of apprehension it becomes fuel I use to capture and bring order and humor to racing thoughts. I move into a sense of "flow" that makes it easy for me to deliver my message.

On the other hand, I used to be paralyzed when I encountered a high open space. For example, one day when I was hiking with a group of friends, we came to a 50 foot long, five foot wide bridge that would be the path over a beautiful cascading waterfall. The stress I experienced bordered on panic.

I think it makes sense to be afraid of falling when walking across a structure above cascading water. My rational brain knew thousands of people had successfully made the walk before. There were hand rails and wire netting high enough on either side of this architectural contraption to assure my safety, but my mind bolted. Ultimately, I held hands with trusty companions as I was coaxed across. When I reached the other side my skin was dry, but my underarms and forehead were soaked with perspiration and the rash on my chest was covered with blisters.

The rest of the beautiful hike, almost ruined by that experience, continued uneventfully. However, like many trigger events, it brought focus to my desire to understand the severity of my reaction that was duplicated when I rode one of those fancy on the outside of a building elevators or climbed open stairs similar to those in the interior of a building. One weekend, wanting to empower myself once again, I put that fear on a rational burner for thoughtful review. Soon insights flooded my brain. The first was that there must be an underlying belief that precipitated a reaction that was somewhat out of proportion to the danger. The second was that I had a choice—even if that choice struggled with some unknown part of me that generated the panic. The third was that if I could change my mind I could overcome the fear in the same way thousands of people have overcome their great fear of public speaking. The fourth was that if I could bring humor to the situation, it would dissipate those catecholamines instead of letting them create havoc in my body.

With permission of the management (who must have thought I was very strange) I spent four hours one day at a warehouse with an open stairwell on the outside wall of a very tall building that had a series of very large windows. I went up one stair at a time, holding on to and looking over the rail then peering outside at adjacent buildings that got smaller and smaller as I went higher and higher. By the time I reached the twentieth floor I was moving faster, with more confidence and realized that my fear was almost gone. Soon I was riding outside elevators and climbing stairs with considerable ease and smiling when I saw someone else experience the panic I knew so well.

Some time later I went with a friend to the top of Empire State Building confident I could manage the experience. I couldn't. I'll leave those romantic rides to Meg Ryan and Tom Hanks (Sleepless in Seattle).

If you have ever blushed with embarrassment, reddened with anger, turned white with fear, developed a rash when you were anxious, or experienced an eruption of acne when under pressure, you know that your skin is a mirror of your life. Stress can make your skin itch, burn or perspire.

Those reactions are potent reminders that our mind and body are linked and how we live our life exerts a profound influence upon our health *and* our beauty. Since research has verified that our attitudes, beliefs and emotional states can trigger chain reactions that affect the activity of every cell and organ of the body, including our skin, it behooves smart women to learn the true meaning of stress management.

Stress is a term that's tossed about casually to describe a wide range of ills. It is drawn from the Latin word that translates "to draw tight." For years we were taught we must avoid stress. Now research has shown that:

✓ there are two kinds of stress: negative stress (too much to do in too little time, losing a loved one, retiring from a meaningful job); and positive stress, called eustress (the prospect of a new home, new job, new relationship);

✓ too little stress can also be disastrous;
✓ stress is inevitable;
✓ we can channel stress into positive and meaningful experiences;
✓ stress can be managed if we "change our minds."

If stress is inevitable, if its energy can be harnessed and redirected and if we have the power to change our minds, life can be a series of beautiful experiences.

One of my most popular lectures is, "Stress, A Humorous Perspective on a Serious Subject." In it I run through some of the irrational thoughts that are a natural part of too many women's every day lives. For example, how many of us spend too much time:

✓ living with an unrealistic sense of urgency ("I must get this done now");
✓ worrying in the past (you can't change it);
✓ worrying in the future (do you *really* know what is going to happen?);
✓ labeling ourselves ("I'm so fat");
✓ overgeneralizing ("I don't have a thing to wear," "I have to do everything" or "I can't put on makeup");
✓ awfulizing or catastrophizing ("It will never work out,\" "It's going to be a long day");
✓ shoulding on ourselves ("I should have...," "I should be...");
✓ self-demeaning thoughts ("I'm no good," "I can't do anything right.");
✓ refusing to say "no," or "I've had enough," or "I *choose* not to do that."

These self-inflicted stress producers are thoughts we can live without. Stress is inevitable. How we manage it is not. Every day we have the choice to let it drag us down or boost us up. Why choose to be fatalistic when life can be fantastic? The media is filled with inspirational and motivating stories of people who overcame stressful adversity by changing their mind, who chose to be visionaries instead of victims and decided that a negative experience did not have to define their life.

There is probably no skin care program that can overcome the adversity that is, too often, precipitated by our irrational mind. Like anything else, part of looking great is ridding yourself of the belief that you don't or can't or won't. The added benefit to positive thinking is that when you add it to good skin care you will have more courage to try something new and daring. That breeds the self-confidence that makes you look even better. It's a winning, versus a self-defeating cycle.

You are your own best stress reduction provider. Balance comes with healthy stress management. Start with a deep breath. Since "holding my breath" is one of the first things I do when I'm stressed, breathing deeply is a habit I have consciously built into my daily life. Now, anytime one of my girlfriends is scared or upset or stressed in any way, I encourage her to stop everything, inhale deeply through her nose and exhale fully through her mouth. Somehow it brings a sense of calmness, if only for a short time, in difficult situations. In those calm moments that breath may allow you to focus your energy so you can respond and move and, even as you respect the dangers of the stress, harness its benefits.

One more thing. One more word: sleep. If your job required a lot of reading it would make a lot of sense to learn to speed read. If your life contains a lot of stress, it makes a lot of sense to do something that can quickly give you a respite and re-store your resiliency skills. Sleep, or at the very least, a power nap, when you are under the fire stress ignites, allows you to quickly get some restorative rest. It is an opportunity to make that deep breathing last a little longer. It brings meaning to mother's encouragement to "Be sure to get your beauty sleep."

A power nap does not mean you need to find a bed in the middle of the day. You can learn to close your eyes and mentally take yourself someplace else for a few minutes. In my sleepless years during college I trained myself to fall asleep on command and wake up in twenty minutes without an alarm clock. It is a skill that continues to make me a sleeping beauty at the drop of a hat. A power nap not only relaxes the mind, it relaxes the body. With practice (or coaching from a hypnotherapist, for example) you, too, can learn to recharge your batteries in a few minutes a day, and spare yourself the burnout of the constant use of the same brain and body circuits. These skills will also be helpful in nudging you, quickly, to restorative and healing dreamland at night.

Sleep is the time and place where and when your body slows down sufficiently to heal and repair itself. In the best case scenario your sleeping hours should be consecutive. If you can function well on four or five hours sleep a night (that means lack of sleep isn't creating more stress) use this gift of extra time to work (or play) passionately at something that makes your soul soar, not something that brings more stress to your life.

In short, managing stress (and sleep) can be one of your most significant beauty definers.

> There is a good reason why mother called getting your rest your "beauty sleep."

Stress Savvy

If you don't get enough stress:

✓ you have no challenges
✓ can gain no confidence
✓ have no opportunity to connect with others (including your intuitive inner wisdom)

28

Beauty from Within

There was a kind of offbeat edge to Leah. She is one of the most beautiful women I know, yet each time I saw her I had this vague feeling that something I couldn't see was troubling her. Because that something didn't "fit" Leah's outer beauty, it troubled me too.

We crossed paths often and became friends. One day she shared pictures of a trip she'd recently taken with a husband who was obviously proud to have this lovely, but very shy, woman on his arm. In several of the photos they were dressed in fashionable and expensive formal wear. I knew Leah didn't like buying expensive clothes or attending fancy social events, so the pictures were somehow out of character. Still, I commented, truthfully, "You look stunning. You are so beautiful." Leah, shyly, looked down and away from the photo album. "I don't think of myself as beautiful," she said, reluctant to accept the compliment.

That was it. Leah looked beautiful from the outside in, but inside—inside her Self—she felt otherwise. As she saw her

Self, what was hidden by her outer beauty was a literally ugly, sad secret.

Where, I wondered, was Leah's self-esteem? Since how we feel about ourselves affects every aspect of our experience, how could someone who believed herself to be unattractive look beautiful? Suddenly I realized her projection of shyness and her unwillingness to spend money on her clothes brought to the outside what she was feeling within.

Psychologist Abraham Mazlow, Ph.D., was the first person to introduce the well-accepted theory that self-esteem is fundamental to promote and maintain mental and emotional well being. In short, it is an essential requirement for a fulfilling, meaningful, beautiful life.

Few of us are passive receptacles for others views of us, so our self-esteem can be fostered externally by others— "Good job," "I like you," "You are a winner," or our personal self-concept—"I'm O.K." "That was good enough," "I did the best I could under the circumstances." Likewise, negative comments erode self-esteem unless we are sufficiently self-assured and self-confident (assuming those don't cross the line into defensive grandiosity or arrogance).

Regardless, to be truly beautiful, in the same way we must breathe and think for ourselves, we must also believe, deep in our heart of hearts, that we are worthy of all we have. Knowledge, skill, material possessions, parenthood, charitable endeavors and cosmetic surgery can, indeed, make us feel better about ourselves. Likewise, projecting an image of beauty, assurance and poise can fool people most of the time, but we must, in the end, find our beauty within.

There are many paths to that radiant inner self that can't be physically seen or touched but is mentally and emotionally palpable. Whether you have embraced it or not, it is that part of you that knows the difference each time you must choose between what is right and wrong—for you.

I can't imagine life without my connection to that untouchable, invisible part of me that believes each of us has a purpose and are part of a divine plan. This isn't necessarily about religion, though religion can be a very personal and meaningful path to experiencing our own unique spiritual awareness. Let's call this awareness spirituality.

Her Story

One of my favorite authors is Rabbi Harold Kushner, author of When Bad Things Happen to Good People. *A Speaking of Women's Health girlfriend, who learned this, sent me an essay he wrote entitled, "The Cure For Despair." In it Kushner relays a Jewish teaching that when God created the world he left it a little bit unfinished, so that we could become His partners in the creative process. Kushner writes: "The sages tell us that 'God could have made a world in which bread grew out of the ground. Instead He made wheat grow, so that the people might turn it into bread.' God could have filled the world with houses, as He provides homes for animals. Instead He filed the earth with trees and stones, with which we can build homes."*

 **This, to me, exemplifies the concept of self-esteem. We have to do the work. We can gather all the knowledge in this and other books about skin, sun protection, moisturizers, makeup, cosmetic surgery, exercise, healthy food and dressing for our roles in life, but it means nothing if we don't, first, radiate from within.**

If you want to touch that spiritual place, capture your inner essence and connect it to your outer beauty, you must pay attention. One of my great teachers challenged me to spend 24 hrs without talking about anyone or anything unless

I had something positive to say. I learned to listen—to that place I found myself, silently now, paying attention to. And I heard something going on within myself that I could have heard long ago. I heard the ongoing struggle between my very loud ego and that soft inner voice which, when I act in concert with it, allows me to be true to myself. That silent, enlightening whole day and night I met the authentic Me. And made a new friend.

Perhaps you think you haven't heard or met your spiritual inner voice. Think again. Pretend you are on a diet. You've made a commitment to avoid sugary, fat desserts. Soon the test comes. There is a piece of cake ready for your enjoyment. You reach out. Within nanoseconds the urge to succumb to an act that flies in the face of your commitment awakens that place inside that thrives when you live in tune with it and tempers the potential for good self-esteem when you don't. That is your spirit talking to you. In order to eat the cake you must ignore, quiet, shut down or, literally, "stuff" that voice. The immediate gratification may feel good, but the price you will pay, later, is realization that you have compromised your integrity and, by doing so, also compromised getting to know your true self. The voice may be soft at first, but if ignored, be assured: it will get louder. Soon you will get a whack on the side of the head. If you still choose to ignore it, a more powerful experience is certain to get your attention. Your spirit wants the good life.

Once you learn to be a true companion to your spirit it becomes easier to respond actively and positively and continue to nurture that inner guide. Your self-esteem and spiritual self blossoms. When that happens, a bad hair day, bloating, abs that aren't flat or any of the other physical "outer" things that used to temper your sense of self can't destroy your smile and the inner beauty certain to be translated to the outside.

Now it is time for you to do the work to nurture and

grow into a vibrant you. Even if you don't know it yet, you are beautiful. You are the piece of cake. The outer stuff is icing! It makes the cake better but without it the cake is still delicious. You are too.

29

The Big Finish

Her Story

Writing a book is an exhilarating and exhausting experience that often requires living in contrast to some of the advice in this book. After I finish a manuscript I give it to friends and editors to read, then take a welcome breather for a few days until feedback trickles in. Soon I return to the writing and self-editing process, rewrite, refine, punch up, tone down and add what my thoughts and dreams have, literally divinely inspired me to add or subtract.

On the day I walked away from this project I celebrated by having a lengthy "let's catch up" lunch with a friend who supported me through the process. By the time lunch was over the unusually cold Pacific Northwest day was showering the streets with snow. We walked home slowly. It was beautiful but having, finally, relaxed, I arrived feeling chilled to the bone. My muscles, having finally "let go" reminded me I was ready for an "at home spa experience." I took my own best advice and settled into a scented stress-reducing bath. Afterward, I wrapped myself in a thick terry bathrobe, had a cup of cocoa, slipped a soothing CD into my bedside music machine, removed the bathrobe and slid into a bed covered with several of my favorite nurturing quilts to stay warm. Sleep quickly followed.

Two hours later I awakened drenched with sweat. I am way past the night sweats stage of menopausal life. As I threw off my covers and sat up, I chuckled remembering how many nights, earlier in life, I had that experience. This time it brought a big smile and awesome respect for a body that could respond so quickly to too many quilts by producing so much sweat I would have to shower again then change my sheets.

Our skin suit is, indeed, an impressive organ. The thought of how many sensory fibers and nerve endings recorded the external heat, how many neurons were fired to tell the body to produce that sweat, how many glands delivered it, how many bacteria were born and died, how many blood vessels expanded or contracted, what happened to my heart rate, blood pressure, respiration and the wonder that it all happened while I slept gives new meaning to the word miracle.

No more fear. Our skin is working. Our brains need some help. As Walter Kelly's cartoon character, Pogo, said, "We have met the enemy and it is us."

The experience of aging and "what is beauty? "is currently (and needlessly) full of harmful myths, negative expectations, stereotypes and prejudices. They play themselves out in many ways. For example, in my lectures I often ask my audience, "How many of you have always been truthful about your age?" The question generates titters, laughter and very few raised hands. Later, I often hear amusing anecdotes of the circumstances under which the "little white lie"was told. Perpetuating a myth about our age only emphasizes how important it has become in our culture to be young. Ads tell us that we can look younger and feel younger than our age despite the fact we cannot turn back time. Still, we continue to have some preconceived notions related to age and what it should look like.

We often, consciously and unconsciously, play out this experience of equating age and beauty. For example, since I'm not married, friends often ask me if I would like to be "fixed up" with one of their single male friends. If I respond, "tell me about him," I am often told his age and what he "does." If this is not familiar to you perhaps you've found yourself in the middle of an equally telling experience. You meet someone and, eventually, you wonder how old he or she is. If, later, you learn that person's true age, you may be surprised, because they exhibit maturity, they are so young. Perhaps the surprise is that they are so "old" since they "act young for their age." Regardless, several judgements, based on what your perception of age-related behavior should be, may come to mind:

If the person has managed, in our judgment, "to stay so young" we may find ourselves thinking, or saying, "I hope I look as good as you do when I reach your age."

If our ages are comparable but our friend seems "younger" than we do, we may wonder, "Why don't I do what is necessary to seem younger than my age?"

If the person looks older than his or her years we wonder, "What happened?" We may even use the information to buoy and affirm our own self worth, thinking, "Thank goodness I took care of myself."

This is a prime example of the relationship between inner and outer age. If we focus on one or another we can get into trouble. For example, I once knew a beautiful woman who was the envy of her generation. She was a successful model in local fashion shows and advertisements, recognized and complimented wherever she went. Because these compliments were about her looks she believed herself to be defined by her beauty.

When she reached her fifties she was still in great demand. Despite that, because that identity was wrapped in her face and body she chose to have some new surgery to enhance her facial features. Sadly, something went wrong. After recovery from a staph infection, part of her face was paralyzed. Her career was over. She disappeared. Later I learned she'd become something of a hermit. Without her good looks her entire self-image was destroyed. For her, the myths she accepted as truths marked the end of what had been a wonderful lifestyle.

On the other hand I've also met people who think their internal beauty is so powerful it can outweigh any exterior challenges. This opposite end of the pendulum is also a set up for failure because life can change on a dime. Our outward beauty or inward beauty is, indeed, a large part of who we are, but it is not *who* we are. True beauty requires meshing the two.

By 2020, one fifth of our population will be 60 and older. We do, indeed, want to "die young at an old age," and want every bit of advice available to make it happen. That gives us a great opportunity to seize this moment. Use the information you've captured here and create a plan. Consider the one significant contributing factor self-made entrepreneurs and great businesses use to generate success, regardless of their field. They make a plan. In the same way you get out a map before you drive from your hometown to some distant destination you can, with a personally styled entrepreneurial attitude, choose to design the destiny for your inner and outer beauty in advance. This means taking into account much more about who you are than what you look like. You can reinvent your lifestyle—and write your own "her story."

One final truth: As you bring yourself into harmony and balance with yourself—physically, mentally, socially, emotionally and spiritually—you will be taking part in the most important and rewarding creative process of your life. You will BE your lifestyle and your destiny. And it will show—from the depths of your being, and your life-loving attitude, all the way out to your wonder-filled skin.

What a joyful lifestyle to look forward to!

Epilogue

It has been six months since the intriguing conversation that precipitated this book. Along the way I have learned much about skin anatomy and physiology, sun, sun damage, skin diseases, the medicines that affect the condition and color of skin, how and why it changes, what, in truth, can be done to decelerate skin changes, the cosmetic industry, how to apply makeup, cosmetic surgery and more. I've talked to hundreds of women, read research reports, looked at too many skin books and websites and attempted to find that fine line between what does and doesn't make us look and feel good about ourselves. The adventure has precipitated many introspective moments, shared stories, and conversations with women (and men) about what makes us radiant to ourselves and to others.

This is typical of the Speaking of Women's Health (SWH) experience. On the provider side of the event, speakers immerse themselves in a subject, collect and study information, review research, consult experts (if they are not the expert themself), ferret fact from fiction, then organize the pertinent and useful material into edu-taining presentations for delivery at a Speaking of Women's Health event. Here they meet women who, in blind faith, invest a day of their life, often without knowing what to expect, in hopes they will walk away with life-changing information.

In the last year, the Speaking of Women's Health Foundation forged a relationship with Lifetime Television for Women. It is a marriage made in heaven because, at last, a message many of us first heard on that network, can be translated from the TV screen into a personal and shared transforming experience. It is true:

"The more you know, the healthier you will be."

My SWH girlfriends and I were in more than 20 cities in 2000. In 2001 many of us are looking forward to visiting an additional fifteen. Speaking of Women's Health is growing and we are growing with it. Personally, this is passionate work that brings purpose to my existence. It fuels and inspires the energies and inspiration to treat my body, mind and spirit with thoughtful respect. Each Speaking of Women's Health get-together is an opportunity to alert and awaken that energy in women by sharing my truth and listening to them share theirs. These gatherings are reminders and also "re-minders" for us that with truth and understanding there is possibility — no probability — that, in spite of chronological aging, LIFE will get better, not worse. The systems of the body may slow but an active lifestyle can prevent the mind from slowing. Learning, via interactive and personal experiences, how to treat dis-ease by educating women to make informed decisions about their health, well-being and safety is an important step to prepare us for the adversities *and* opportunities certain to come our way. We become more than humans doing. We are humans being.

Helen Keller wrote, "The best and most beautiful things in the world cannot be seen or even touched — they must be felt with the heart."

Touching one anothers' hearts is what girlfriends do best. It ignites and fuels a bright flame in that mysterious beautiful place within that can light the path to self-fulfillment and self-confidence and radiate your authentic beauty to the whole world.

Will you join us? Also visit http://www.speakingofwomenshealth.com to feel the sense of quality experience, luxury and camaraderie that is Speaking of Women's Health.

Glossary

Acne: chronic inflammation of the sebaceous glands

Adipose Tissue: Fat

AHA: See alpha hydroxy acids

Alpha Hydroxy Acids (AHAs): that group of skin care products used to exfoliate the skin by removing dead skin cells

Age Spot: irregular spots of skin hyperpigmentation; also called liver spots or sun spots

Antioxidant: an agent that retains chemical stability of cells

Beta Hudroxy Acid (BHA): a misnomer for salicylic acid—used to accelerate the turnover of skin cells

Blackhead: a plug of sebum exposed to oxidizing air that turns it black

Broad Spectrum Sun Protection: protects against both UVA and UVB rays of the sun

Cancer: uncontrolled, abnormal growth of cells

Ceramide: a synthetic lipid (fat) that helps retain skin moisture

Collagen: a protein found in the dermis that gives the skin elasticity and firmness; in skin care products it works like a humectant

Comedone: a plug of hardened sebum and dirt around the base of a hair follicle

Dermatitis: inflammation of the skin

Dermatologist: a physician who specializes in diseases of the skin

Dermatology: the study of skin, its nature, functions, structures, diseases and treatments

Dermis: the thicker under-layer of the skin

Diagnosis: the recognition of a disease by its symptoms

Eczema: acute or chronic, dry or moist lesions of unknown cause

Elastin: the tissue, in the dermis, responsible for skin resilience and flexibility; in skin care products it helps keep skin moist

Epidermis: the thin, outer layer of the skin

Etiology: the study of the causes of disease

Exfoliate: the removal of dead skin cells of the epidermis

Humectant: a substance that absorbs or helps another substance retain moisture

Lesion: a structural change in the tissues caused by injury or disease

Liver Spot: see age spot

Melanin: the substance in the epidermis that determines skin color

Moisturizer: reduces moisture loss from the skin by forming a water-impenetrable barrier on its surface

Mole: a small, brownish to black blemish on the skin

Nutraceutical: a vitamin, mineral or other micronutrient packaged and sold as a dietary supplement

Pathology: the study of disease

Phytochemical: a chemical in a plant

Prognosis: the foretelling of a probable course of a disease

Retin-A: retinoic acid; the "brand" name for tretinoin; developed for acne but effective for diminishing wrinkles

Salicylic Acid: a beta hydroxy acid (BHA) used in skin care products

Sebaceous Gland: gland in the dermis that produces oil

Sebum: the oil produced by the sebaceous gland

SPF: abbreviation for sun protection factor—indicates a product's ability to block out the sunburn and cancer-causing UVB rays of the sun

Sweat: moisture excreted through skin

Tea: one of the free radical scavengers that is known to help "calm" the skin

Titamium Dioxide: physical UV blocker, helps block both UVA and UVB wavelengths of light.

T-Zone: skin on the face in the area of the nose and to the right and left on the forehead

Tretinoin: generic name for Retin A, a vitamin A derivative used to treat acne

UVA Rays: the aging rays of the sun

UVB Rays: the (sun) burning rays of the sun

Vitamin A (in skin care): oil/fat soluble vitamin useful for smoothing out dry skin, minimizing pore size and reducing the appearance of fine wrinkle line; causes sun sensitivity

Vitamin B (in skin care): believed to improve effectiveness of other chemicals in a product

Vitamin C (in skin care): a vital antioxidant which appears to stimulate activity in dermis layer of the skin to produces collagen

Vitamin D (in skin care): oil/fat soluble vitamin that helps regulate cell turnover

Vitamin E (in skin care): in the tocopheral form, this oil soluble antioxidant helps to moisturize skin and has some protection against UV light damage

Whitehead: a plug of sebum that remains under the skin

Whitch Hazel: an astringent

Questions for a Cosmetic Surgeon

If you are contemplating cosmetic surgery there are a few things you need to know that I have not found listed in any book.

First of all, your prospective surgeon *must* be board certified by the American Society of Cosmetic and Reconstructive Surgery.

Before you make a decision, visit, and interview, several physician candidates with as much focus as you would use before hiring a caregiver for your child. Take a trusted friend or relative who can take notes during your consultations. After hearing "what you want" and discussing options, your doctor should ask you if you have any questions. Ask:

✓ How long have you been board certified?

✓ What is your favorite procedure? or Which procedures do you perform most frequently? How many of these procedures do you do a week? (More is better.)

✓ What is your privacy policy?

✓ Where are your surgeries performed (hospital or office surgical area)?

✓ If in office, what kind of emergency procedures are you prepared to handle?

✓ Do you perform the entire surgery or do you have assistants?

✓ What kind of anesthesia do you use? Is there an anesthesiologist on site? (This is a best case scenario.)

✓ Have you written any books or articles? (If so, ask for copies, then read them.)

✓ Can you give me the name of any patients I can contact to ask about their experience?

✓ If I have the procedure, how long can I expect the results to last?

✓ Will I have scars? If so, will they show? How long until they fade?
✓ What kind of care will I require after the procedure?
✓ How soon can I go back to work?
✓ What are the risks of my surgery?
✓ How much will this cost?
✓ What does this cost include and exclude?
✓ Do you have financing or do you take credit cards?

Your surgeon's fee will probably not be covered by insurance.

Resources

Books You Can Use

Books About Skin Care

Shelves are lined with books about skin care. Some are oriented to practical use, some are inspiring, some make beautiful coffee table books. Although it was hard to choose, here are a few suggestions:

A Consumer's Dictionary of Cosmetic Ingredients
by Ruth Winter, M. S.

This book is in its fifth printing. It is an encyclopedia of the more than 6000 "ingredients" that are in cosmetic products. I can't imagine how Ruth Winter manages to get this information updated every year. The introduction is worth the price of the book. It is available in most libraries.
Publisher; Crown Trade Paperback
List Price: $14

Ageless Beauty : A Woman's Guide to Lifelong Beauty and Well-Being
by Dayle Haddon

This is one of those books that is not only filled with great information, it is also a pleasure to look at. Haddon's face will be familiar to you as she has had contracts with four major cosmetic companies. This book includes as much information about self-esteem and caring for yourself—even spiritually—as it does about makeup and beauty.
Publisher; Hyperion Press
List Price: $29.95

ESSENCE Total Makeover: Body, Beauty, Spirit
Edited by Patricia Mignon Hinds
There are too few books about beauty written for women of color. This beautiful book celebrates the inner and outer beauty of all women with emphasis on tips for Black women in every shape, size and shade. The photographs are beautiful. The advice is exemplary.
Publisher; Crown
List price: $30.00

Feel Fabulous Forever: The Anti-Aging Health & Beauty Bible
by Josephine Fairley and Sarach Stacey
This beautiful book is expensive, but it is a great choice if you want to be inspired to learn more about any subject related to skin and overall health.
Publisher; The Overlook Press
List Price: $36.00

Looking Good at Any Age : A Woman Dermatologist Talks to Women About What to Expect, What to Accept, What Can Be Changed
by Amy E. Newburger, M.D.
This book is scientifically sound and psychologically exciting. It includes case histories and an overview of many commercial skin products.
Publisher; Doubleday
List Price: $22.95

Total Skin: The Definitive Guide to Whole Skin Care for Life
by David Leffell

    If I had to recommend only one book as a follow-up to *Beauty, More Than Skin Deep* it would be this book. Leffell is an internationally recognized expert in skin cancer and aging. His thick but easy-to-read book is filled with useful sidebars, photos and other illustrations to support the well written comprehensive text that covers skin health, skin care, skin problems, protecting and preserving skin and being smart about skin cancer. There is also a useful overview of what to expect from the latest advances in cosmetic surgery and other methods of making skin look younger than your chronological age.

Publisher; Hyperion
List Price: $27.95

Books About Cosmetic Surgery

There have been many books on this subject published in recent years. Your best bet is to visit a favorite bookstore or your local library to discover if one catches your fancy. Here are a few suggestions:

Everything You Ever Wanted To Know About Cosmetic Surgery But Couldn't Afford To Ask : A Complete Look At The Latest Techniques And Why They Are Safer
by Alan. Gaynor, M.D.

Gaynor is a dermatologist and a plastic surgeon. What is different about this book is its inclusion of inexpensive strategies to take care of yourself so well that you won't need snips and tucks. He also describes procedures.
Publisher; Broadway Books
List Price: $14

LIFT: Wanting, Fearing, and Having A Face-Lift
by Joan Kron

Kron is one of the most respected journalists in the field of cosmetic surgery. This makes her an excellent guide through the identity crisis that occurs when your face no longer fits your self image. There's dozens of real cases, interviews, historical information, years of research and a comprehensive bibliography in this book. The best fun of all is her reference to famous people and the procedures they've had and comments about famous, craggy-faced, older men who have verbalized their desire to avoid facelifts as they marry younger and younger wives. (Think Clint Eastwood.)
Publisher;Viking Press
List Price: $13.95

*The Smart Woman's Guide to Plastic Surgery : Essential
Information from a Female Plastic Surgeon*
By Jean M. Loftus M.D.
    The biggest advantage of this easy to understand book is
that it was written by a female plastic surgeon. It covers more
than just the surgery itself. It also delves into the "what
happens before" and "what happens after."
Publisher; Contemporary Books
List Price: $17

Welcome To Your Facelift
by Helen Bransford
    This easy to read book, with a few illustrations and
pictures, chronicles this 47 year old author's experience with a
forehead peel, upper eyelid tuck, dermabrasion under her eyes
and standard facelift. It is most suited for pre-menopausal
women considering a facelift. She names names. (You know
what I mean.)
Publisher; Doubleday
List Price: $11.95

Books to Help You Get Fit Fast

Fitness for Dummies
by Suzanne Schlosberg, Liz Neporent
    This book is a perfect starter for fitness novices inter-
ested in general fitness information. You will learn everything
you need to know about starting and maintaining a fitness
program—getting motivated, choosing a gym, building
strength and aerobic endurance, and buying home exercise
equipment. These well-known health writers tell it with wit
and style.
Publisher; IDG Books
List Price: $15.99

Strength Training Past 50
by Wayne L. Westcott, Ph.D, Thomas R. Baechle, Mark Williams

Strength training is an equal-opportunity exercise system. Regardless of how old you are when you start, strength training has nearly immediate benefits: more muscle mass, more strength, a higher fat burning metabolism. This book gives older exercisers all the information they need to get started, including advice on testing for strength and how to pick a qualified personal trainer. Fitness expert Wayne Westcott and supporter Tom Baechle present 39 safe and effective exercises as part of a 10-week strength training plan. 130 photos.
Publisher; Human Kinetics
List Price: $13.56

The Ultimate Fit or Fat
by Covert Bailey

Covert Bailey's done it again. He's revised his popular Fit or Fat. Though retired from public speaking, as a writer, Bailey remains at the top of his game. The title is misleading. The perspective is based on the necessity to address fitness issues from the perspective of the fit and not so fit. There is a focus in this edition (the 3rd Fit or Fat) on weight lifting–highly recommended to get a jump start your metabolism. The book includes a guide, with pictures, for a home strength building program.
Publisher; Houghton Mifflin
List Price: $9.95

Weight Training for Dummies
by Suzanne Schlosberg, Liz Neporent

If you want a more strenuous strength-training program using free weights and gym machines, try this book which has plenty of easy-to-understand instructions for beginners, but also includes information for those who've been training a while. It's pumped up with more than 100 photos and illustrations of the best exercises for the major and minor muscle groups—exactly what you need for a balanced strength building workout.

Publisher; IDG Books
List Price: $15.99

Workouts for Dummies
by Tamilee Webb, Lori Seeger

O. K. So you think you can't relate to a buffed star of exercise videos and TV appearances. (Forget your prejudice. Ronda, who knows Tamilee, reports she is the most down-to-earth, enthusiastic motivator you could meet.) This book starts with topics as basic as choosing shoes and warming up. Then it covers everything you'll need to create an effective exercise program, starting with an explanation of body types (so you don't think you'll end up looking like Cindy Crawford if you don't already) and the workouts that suit your body type. The book gives directions for stretches, aerobic exercises, muscle conditioning (using weights, furniture, exercise bands, and bars), and workouts for different locations.

Publisher; IDG Books
List Price: $15.99

Books to Help You Eat Smart

Age Proof Your Body
by Elizabeth Somer, R. D.
When Elizabeth Somer speaks about nutrition, you should listen. She has a clear and approachable style. Her information is gleaned from the research, not hype, so she is careful to point out where science ends and guessing begins. Somer describes very specific ways to eat better for the purpose of heading off age-related diseases and dysfunctions.
Publisher; Quill
List Price: $14

Nutrition Nuggets
by Ronda Gates
Although this book is ten years old, it is filled with useful information for women of all ages seeking to improve their mind and body when it comes to nutrition. In addition to easy-to-read, never out of date text about caffeine, salt, sugar, the various fats, supermarket savvy, and restaurant survival there are ten motivating stories about women who struggled and made lifestyle change.
Publisher; 4-Heart Press
List Price: $11.95
It is available for $5 to Speaking of Women's Health readers. Call (800) 863-6000 or visit Ronda's website: http://www.rondagates.com for a copy.

Smart Eating
by Ronda Gates and Covert Bailey
This book is designed for anyone who wants to eat smart—men & women, vegetarians, people with weight problems, athletes, healthy people, and even those with medical problems like osteoporosis and diabetes. It offers an

alternative to dieting with a revolutionary way to think about food as nutrition. The process is simplified by the Smart Eating "Food Target" — a unique graphic that grades foods according to their fat and fiber content. It includes 200 recipes keyed to the Food Target. You'll never diet again.
Publisher; Houghton Mifflin Paperback
List Price: $9.95
Call (800) 863-6000 or visit Ronda's website:
http://www.rondagates.com for a discounted copy plus a free Smart Eating poster.

Home Exercise Videos

http://www.collagevideo.com
This site offers a 60-90 second preview of the several hundred videos they stock. They also have a paper catalog that describes every video available and a toll free service with telephone representatives who can help you choose the video that matches your needs and fitness level. Call (800) 433-6769 or email collage@collagevideo.com for a catalog.

http://www.homeworkout.com
There is no catalog for this company and no toll free consultation service but they have a slightly different selection of videos, sell some books, and exercise equipment and offer profiles of exercise leaders.

Internet Sites

Information about Cosmetic Surgery
American Board of Plastic Surgery
http://www.abplsurg.org
Phone: (215) 587-9322

American Society for Aesthetic Plastic Surgery
http://www.surgery.org
Phone: (888) 272-7711

American Society for Dermatatologic Surgery
http://www.asds-net.org
Phone: (800) 330-1090

American Society of Plastic and Reconstructive Surgeons
http://www.plasticsurgery.org
Phone: (847) 228-9900

American Association of Facial Plastic and Reconstructive
Surgeons
http://www.facial-plastic-surery.org
Phone: (800) 332-323

American Society for Laser Medicine and Surgery
http://www.aslms.org
Phone: (715) 845-9283

Information about Skin Care and Dermatology:
American Society for Dermatologic Surgery
http://www.asds-net.org
Phone: (800) 330-1090

American Academy of Dermatology (AAD)
http://www.aad.com
Phone: (847) 330-0230

Kids Connection

This special section of the American Academy of Dermatology's Web site provides children, ages eight through adolescence, with information about dermatology.

Mayo Clinic

This is a trusted organization that provides comprehensive and practical resources for all things medical, including skin care.

Information about Healthy Eating:

American Dietetic Association Infoline:
http://www.eatright.org

Go here to get accurate information about nutrition. It is the professional organization for registered dietitians. Phone: (800) 336-1655

Information about Skin Cancer

The Skin Cancer Foundation
http://www.aoa.dhhs.gov/aoa/dir/219.html
Phone: (800) SKIN-490 (1-800-754-6490)

This nonprofit, public information organization works to educate the public about the importance of detecting and treating skin cancer as early as possible. It also provides support for medical training and research.

American Institute of Cancer Research Nutrition Hotline:
http://www.aicr.org

This site offers news, research updates, recipes, free publications and tips to help you live a healthier, cancer-free life. Phone: (800) 843-8114

National Cancer Institute (NCI)

http://www.nci.nih.gov/

This site offers information about cancer, provides resources for scientists and issues press releases about cancer related subjects. Phone: (301) 435-3848

Information about Women's Health

LIFESTYLES by Ronda Gates

http://www.rondagates.com

This site, hosted by *Beauty, More Than Skin Deep* author and Speaking of Women's Health keynoter, Ronda Gates, is packed with information about a variety of women's health issues. There is a free fitness tip and free recipe daily, an osteoporosis and a heart disease risk profile, and a calculator that will reveal how many calories you need to eat to get and keep a realistic weight. Registration for Gates' complimentary weekly Email Newsletter will get you a download of low fat, easy-to-fix recipes. Write to: LIFESTYLES by Ronda Gates, P. O. Box 974, Lake Oswego, OR 97034. Phone: (503) 697-7572

Speaking of Women's Health (SWH)

http://www.speakingofwomenshealth.com,

http://www.swh.net;

I love this organization. If you have attended a Speaking of Women's Health conference you know why. Each year the non-profit foundation manages conferences in almost forty cities nationwide for the purpose of educating women to make better informed decisions about their health, well-being and safety. Their web site lists conference sites. You will also learn more about their 2001 initiative, skin care and self-esteem as well as many other subjects covered in previous years. There is streaming video of keynotes, reviews of presentations by the prestigious speakers at each event and useful health information for use in your daily life.

For more information about SWH Write to: Speaking of Women's Health Foundation, Kathy DeLaura, Executive Director, 1223 Central Parkway, Cincinnati, OH 45214-2890. Phone: (513) 345-6570

Sites with Information about Cosmetic Surgery

John Hopkins Hospital
http://www.med.jhu.edu/plasticsurg/
Information on Johns Hopkins Department of Plastic and Reconstructive Surgery including cosmetic procedures, and an educational section.

The American Society for Aesthetic Plastic Surgery
http://www.surgery.org
If you're curious about the average price of a cosmetic surgery procedure, you can check out a fact sheet provided by this organization.

Cosmetic Doc Shop
http://www.cosmeticsdocshop.com
CosmeticDocshop is a resource that allows patients to learn about cosmetic/plastic surgery, the technology behind cosmetic/plastic surgery procedures, and find a cosmetic/plastic surgery specialist who has a website in their area. The doctors participating in CosmeticDocShop perform all types of cosmetic/plastic surgery including laser cosmetic surgery, facial plastic surgery, breast augmentation, rhino-plasty, implants for the entire body, hair transplants, laser skin resurfacing, liposculpture and chemical peels.

Smoking Cessation Programs

Ready, Set, Stop
    Registered nurse, health educator Fern Carness, a former smoker, has created a 4-tape audio series, program worksheets, food and activity planners, and other materials to help smokers stop their smoking habit.
http://www.readysetstop.com or call: (800) 950-9355 or write: P. O. Box 509, Lake Oswego, OR 97034

Smokenders
    "SMOKENDERS is an educational program having as its goal, not only the cessation of smoking, but of enjoying not smoking and being comfortable as a nonsmoker."
9617 N.W. Golden Avenue, Vancouver, WA 98665
Phone: (800) 828 HELP
Web Site: http://www.smokenders.com.

Meet Your Authors

Ronda Gates

Ronda Gates, M. S., C. L. C., is a health promotion educator whose company, LIFESTYLES by Ronda Gates, develops and delivers programs and products to support lifestyle change.

In 1978 Ronda exchanged the white coat she wore during her 17 year career as a hospital pharmacist for a pair of athletic shoes and never looked back. Her corporate fitness business precipitated graduate health studies, many prestigious awards and fellowships, and a professional career that reflects her effort to make sense out of the conflicting information, myths, and misconceptions about women's health. Ronda is a prolific writer who has authored many books about health and fitness including her most recent, *Smart Women, Strong Bones.*

When Ronda is not "on the road" lecturing about the many aspects of making healthy lifestyle change, she is writing about it for publication in the press, magazines, and on the internet. She maintains her good health by teaching a daily dance fitness class and "re-creates" in her garden, on a bicycle, and hiking hills nationwide.

Ronda, the mother of two grown children, Rebecca and Caleb, lives in Lake Oswego, OR. You can learn more about her at http://www.rondagates.com. She can be contacted at ronda@rondagates.com or 503-697-7572.

Ethel Harms

After a twenty one year career as a fashion model and modeling school instructor, Ethel Harms was certified as an image consultant and launched Focus On Image, a consulting business specializing in personal image services for professional organizations, social groups and individuals. Her programs include professional appearance, wardrobe and style development, illusion dressing, personal color selection and fashion and commercial makeup artistry.

Ethel is best known for translating her personal experience dealing with her changing skin suit and body shape into practical strategies that can help her clients blossom into confident beauties at all ages. Ethel is more than a consultant, she is a friend to her clients who treat daughters to first time makeup lessons and, subsequently, artistry for their weddings.

Ethel and her husband, Bill, live in Portland, OR. She is mother of two grown sons, Eric and Todd, and the grandmother of Paige Marie.

You can contact her at eharms@msn.com or Focus on Image (503) 665-5318

Joanne Deitz Thompson

Joanne is a talented Apparel Designer and Fashion Illustrator. Her experience providing illustrations and cover design for this book is a new one that, she admits, has been one of her most joyful professional experiences.

Although she describes herself as a "beauty product addict," Joanne believes that she has found her fountain of youth in exercise, fresh air, good nutrition and happiness. She stays fit and healthy by running, walking and doing Pilates. That routine, generated a forty pound weight loss that further defined her beautiful self. Her husband and four year old daughter are intimately involved in that lifestyle experience. Joanne lives in Portland, Oregon.

Joanne can be reached by writing her at: jdtallula@earthlink.net

Profits from the sale of additional copies of *Beauty, More than Skin Deep* will be donated to Speaking of Women's Health Foundation.

There are four convenient ways to order additional copies:
1. On the internet: http://www.rondagates.com
    • A secure site; use Smart Bargains icon

2. By phone: (503) 697-7572
    • Visa and MC accepted

3. By mail: C/O LIFESTYLES 4-Heart Press
    P.O. Box 974
    Lake Oswego, OR 97034

4. Call Speaking of Women's Health   (503) 345-6587

Each book costs $10.
Discounts for multiples of 10 or more.
Add $1.50 per book for regular shipping and handling.
Add $5.00 for priority shipping by USPS.

To ship your book(s) we need:
    Number of copies you wish to purchase
    Your Name
    Your Shipping Address
    Your Phone Number (in case there is a problem) or
    Your Email address
    Your Visa or MC # and expiration date on the card
    The name on the credit card